All-in-One
Student Workbook

Grade 1

Includes:

- Review of key concepts/skills

- Practice for each lesson

- Reteaching for each lesson

Scott Foresman·Addison Wesley

enVisionMATH™

Learning Solutions

New York   Boston   San Francisco
London   Toronto   Sydney   Tokyo   Singapore   Madrid
Mexico City   Munich   Paris   Cape Town   Hong Kong   Montreal

Cover Art: Luciana Navarro Powell

This special edition published in cooperation with Pearson Learning Solutions.

All trademarks, service marks, registered trademarks, and registered service marks are the property of their respective owners and are used herein for identification purposes only.

Pearson Learning Solutions, 501 Boylston Street, Suite 900, Boston, MA 02116
A Pearson Education Company
www.pearsoned.com

Printed in the United States of America

10   17

000200010270780077

CP

ISBN-10: 0-328-62588-4
ISBN-13: 978-0-328-62588-8

Table of Contents

Review From Last Year

Name _____

More, Fewer, As Many As

Cows!

More cows!   **Fewer** cows!   **As many** cows!

Which has more? Draw a circle.

1.

2.

Which has fewer? Draw a circle.

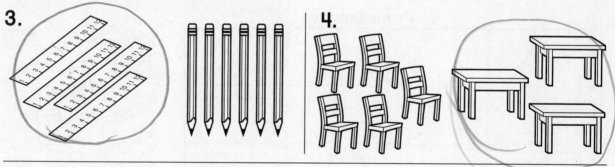

3.

4.

Which has as many? Draw a circle.

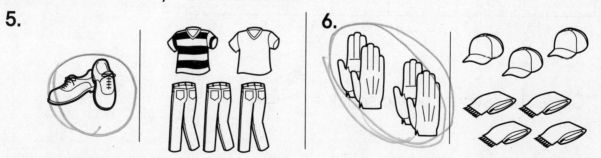

5.

6.

Notes for Home Your child identified groups that have more, fewer, and as many objects than a given group.
Home Activity: Ask your child to make groups of coins with more, fewer, and as many coins as another group.

Name _____

Graphing

Make a bar graph. Color a square for each playground item.

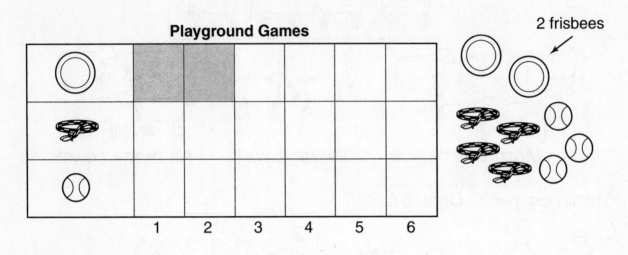

Playground Games

2 frisbees

1. Circle the favorite game.

Complete the bar graph below. Answer the question.

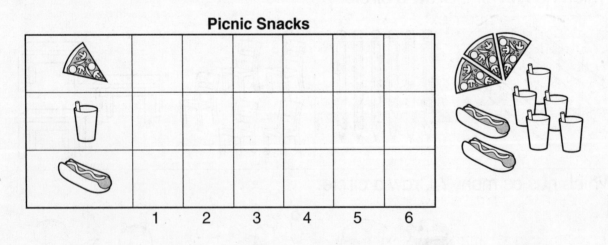

Picnic Snacks

2. Circle the favorite picnic snack.

Problem Solving: Look for a Pattern

Look at the pattern.

What comes next?

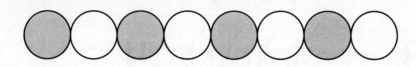

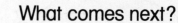
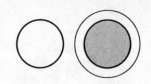

What comes next? Draw a circle.

1.

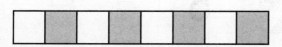

2.

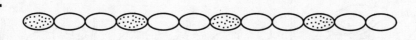

3.

Draw what comes next.

4.

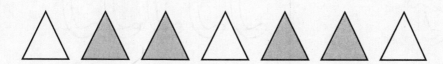   _____

5.

   _____

Notes for Home Your child recognized and colored patterns. *Home Activity:* Ask your child to make a pattern using objects such as coins or buttons.

Name _____

Write Numbers to 5

 1

 2

 3

 4

 5

Write how many.

5

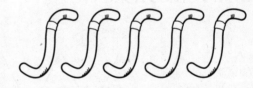

3

1

5

4

2

Notes for Home Your child counted and wrote numbers for groups of 1 to 5 objects. *Home Activity:* Ask your child to show you groups of objects for the numbers up to 5.

Compare Numbers to 5

less than 5   **5**   **more than 5**

How many? Circle the answer.

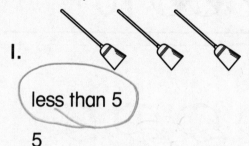

1.

(less than 5)

5

more than 5

2.

less than 5

(5)

more than 5

3.

less than 5

5

(more than 5)

4.

(less than 5)

5

more than 5

5.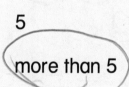

less than 5

5

(more than 5)

6.

less than 5

(5)

more than 5

Notes for Home Your child identified whether groups of objects showed less than 5, 5, or more than 5.
Home Activity: Ask your child to show groups of objects that are less than 5, equal to 5, and more than 5.

Write Numbers to 10

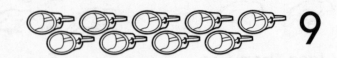

6   7

8   9

10

Write how many.

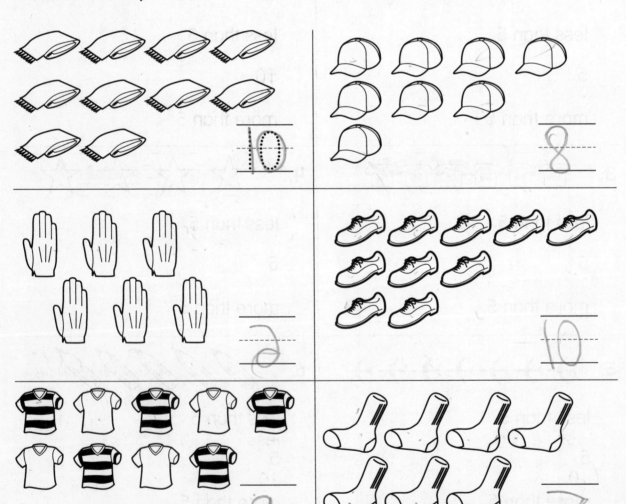

Notes for Home Your child counted and wrote numbers for groups of 1 to 10 objects. *Home Activity:* Ask your child to show you groups of objects for the numbers up to 10. Have them write numbers for each group.

6

Name _____

Compare Numbers to 10

less than 10   10   more than 10

How many? Circle the answer.

1.

less than 10

10

(more than 10)

2.

(less than 10)

10

more than 10

3.

less than 10

(10)

more than 10

4.

(less than 10)

10

more than 10

5.

less than 10

(10)

more than 10

6.

less than 10

10

(more than 10)

Notes for Home Your child identified whether groups of objects showed less than 10, 10, or more than 10.
Home Activity: Ask your child to show groups of objects that are less than 10, equal to 10, and more than 10.

Length

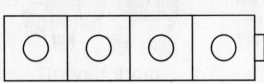

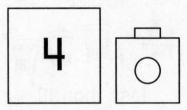

4

Write how many  each object measures.

1.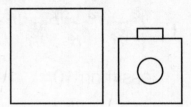

2.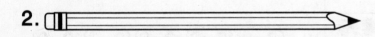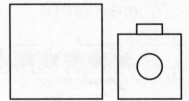

3.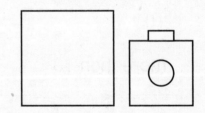

4.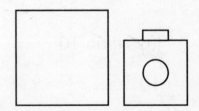

Notes for Home Your child used cubes to measure lengths of objects, then wrote the length of each object.
Home Activity: Ask your child to measure objects such as books and pencils using paper clips.

Name _____

Capacity

MILK

holds more   **holds less**

Circle which holds more. Cross out which holds less.

1.

2.

3.

4.

5.

6.

Notes for Home Your child compared sets of containers and identified which container holds more.
Home Activity: Ask your child to choose two containers at home and identify which holds more. Test their prediction with water.

Name _____

Weight

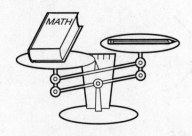 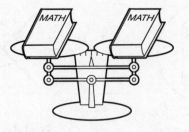 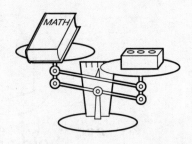

lighter than book   **weighs the same**   **heavier than book**

Draw a line from the object to the correct scale.

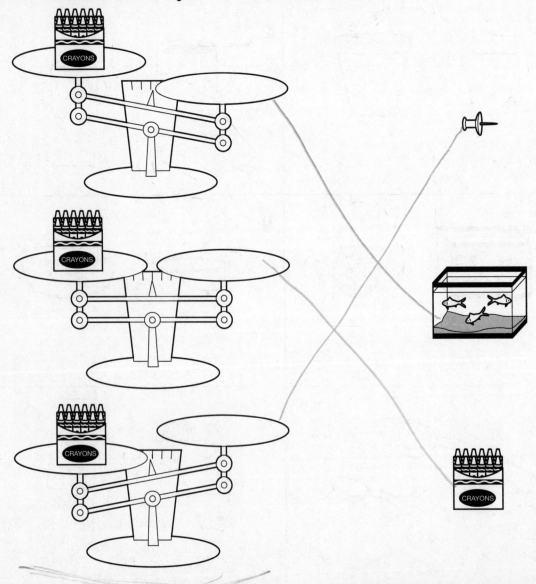

© Pearson Education, Inc. 1

Notes for Home Your child identified objects that were lighter than, weighed the same as, or were heavier than given objects. *Home Activity:* Ask your child to show objects that are lighter than, weigh the same as, and are heavier than a can of soup.

Solids

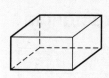 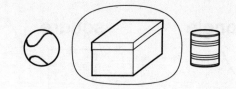

Circle the object that looks like the solid.

1.      

2. 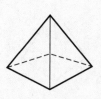   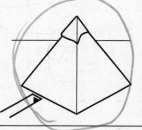   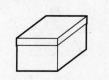

3.      

4.   

5.   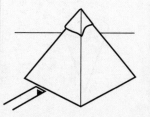      

Notes for Home Your child found objects that were the same shape as boxes, cones, pyramids, cans, and balls.
Home Activity: Ask your child to identify solid shapes found in objects at home.

Shapes

circle   triangle   square   rectangle

Color the flat surface of the solid that matches the shape.

1.

2.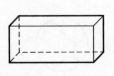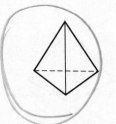

3.

4.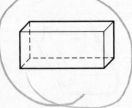

5.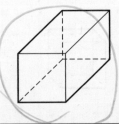

Notes for Home Your child found shapes in solids. *Home Activity:* Help your child trace the shape of one side of a box or can.

Name _____

Equal Parts

equal parts   not equal parts

   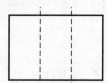   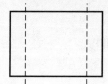

Circle pictures that show equal parts.

Cross out pictures that do not have equal parts.

1. 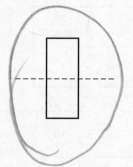   2. 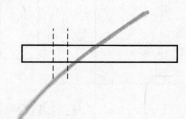   3.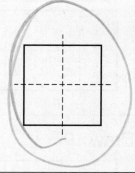

4. 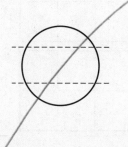   5. 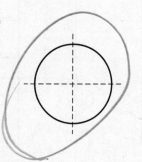   6.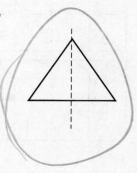

Draw lines to show equal parts.

7.   8.   9.

Numbers to 20

0 1 2 3 4 5 6 7 8 9 10 11 12 13 14 15 16 17 18 19 20

Draw how many.

1. Draw 14.

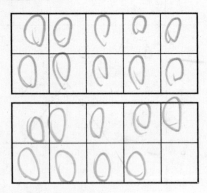

2. Draw 17.

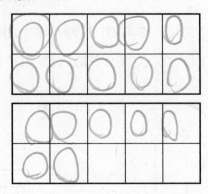

3. Draw 19.

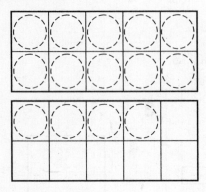

4. Draw 12.

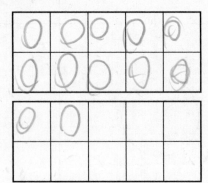

Write how many.

5.

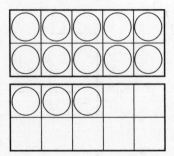

13

6.

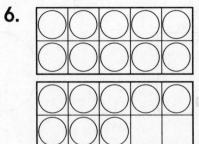

18

Notes for Home Your child showed and identified numbers up to 20 on ten-frames. *Home Activity:* Ask your child to count to 20 using pennies or buttons.

Name _____

Sums to 10

$$3 \quad + \quad 4 \quad = \quad 7$$

Write number sentences. Add.

1.

   | 2 | + | 3 | = | |

2.

   | | + | | = | |

3.

   | | + | | = | |

4.

   | | + | | = | |

5.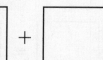

   | | + | | = | |

6.

   | | + | | = | |

Notes for Home Your child wrote number sentences to tell an addition story for each picture. *Home Activity:* Ask your child to draw his or her own addition story. Have him or her write a number sentence for the story.

Differences to 10

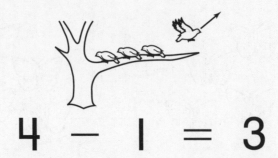

$$4 - 1 = 3$$

Write number sentences. Subtract.

1.

| 5 | − | 1 | = | |

2.

| 7 | − | | = | |

3.

| 6 | − | | = | |

4.

| 10 | − | | = | |

5.

| 4 | − | | = | |

6.

| 9 | − | | = | |

Notes for Home Your child wrote number sentences to tell a subtraction story for each picture. *Home Activity:* Ask your child to draw his or her own subtraction story. Have him or her write a number sentence for the story.

Reteaching and Practice

0 to 5

 There are many ways I can show a number. I can draw a picture. Then I can count how many and write the number.

1   2   3

4   5   0

Count how many. Circle the number.

1.

0   (1)   2   3   4   5

2.

0   1   2   3   4   5

Number Sense

3. Use 3 different ways to show a number.

0 to 5

Write the number that tells how many.

1.

_____
- - - - - - - - -
_____

2.

_____
- - - - - - - - -
_____

3.

_____
- - - - - - - - -
_____

4. Which tells how many?

Ⓐ 1
Ⓑ 2
Ⓒ 3
Ⓓ 4

Number Sense

Draw a picture.
Write the number.

5. Peggy has some hats.

_____
- - - - - - - - -
_____

6. Daniel has some books.

_____
- - - - - - - - -
_____

6 to 10

Use your hands to show each number.

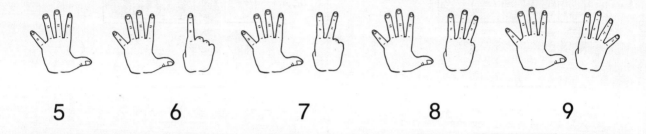

| 5 | 6 | 7 | 8 | 9 |

Put a counter on each animal.
Count the counters.
Write the number that tells how many.

1. _6_

2. _____

3. _____

6 to 10

Write the number that tells how many.

1.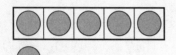

_____
- - - - - - -
_____

2.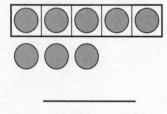

_____
- - - - - - -
_____

3.

_____
- - - - - - -
_____

4.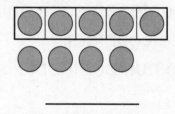

_____
- - - - - - -
_____

5. Kat saved 5 pennies.
Then she saved 2 more.
How many pennies did
she save?

Ⓐ 7

Ⓑ 8

Ⓒ 9

Ⓓ 10

Algebra

6. Draw more counters
to make 10.

10, 11, and 12

You can use sets of 5 to make 10, 11, or 12.

10	11	12
ten	eleven	twelve

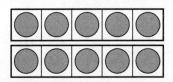
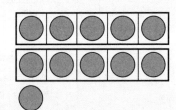
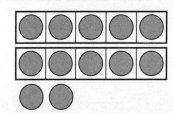

Count the bugs.
Write the number that tells how many.

1.

‐ ‐ ‐ ‐ ‐ ‐ ‐ ‐

2.

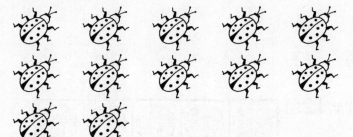

_____
‐ ‐ ‐ ‐ ‐ ‐
_____

3.

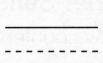

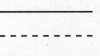

_____
‐ ‐ ‐ ‐ ‐ ‐
_____

10, 11, and 12

Write the number that tells how many.

1.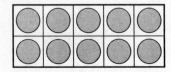

_____

- - - - - - - -

_____

2.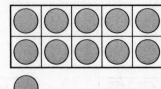

_____

- - - - - - - -

_____

3. Which number tells how many?

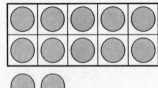

Ⓐ 13

Ⓑ 12

Ⓒ 11

Ⓓ 10

Number Sense

4. Draw counters to show 12.

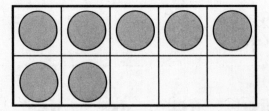

Name_____

Spatial Patterns for Numbers to 9

You can use patterns to show numbers.

You can use patterns to compare numbers.

This pattern shows 3.

This pattern shows 6.

Write the number the pattern shows.

I.

_____

- - - - - - -

2.

_____

- - - - - - -

3.

_____

- - - - - - -

4.

_____

- - - - - - -

Journal

5. Use 7 squares to make a pattern.

Spatial Patterns for Numbers to 9

Write the number of dots.

1.  _____
_____
_____

2. _____
_____
_____

3. _____
_____
_____

4. _____
_____
_____

5. _____
_____
_____

6. _____
_____
_____

Journal

7. Draw a dot pattern to show
the number of people
in your family.
Then write the number.

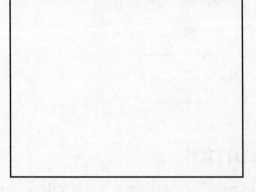

_____
_____ people

Practice 1-4

Spatial Patterns for Numbers to 10

You can use two-part patterns to show numbers.

Use each pattern to tell how many without counting.

This part shows 4.

This part shows 2.

The two parts together show 6 shoes in all.

Circle the number that tells how many in all.

1.

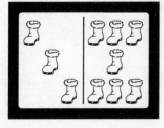

(4) 5 6

2.

6 7 8

3.

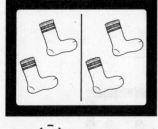

7 9 10

4.

8 10 12

Algebra

5. Draw the missing dot pattern for 9.

Reteaching 1-5

Spatial Patterns for Numbers to 10

Write the number that tells how many.

1.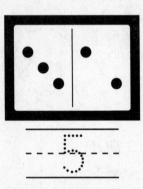

_____
5
- - - - - -
_____

2.

_____
- - - - - - - -
_____

3.

_____
- - - - - - - -
_____

4.

_____
- - - - - - - -
_____

5.

_____
- - - - - - - -
_____

6.

_____
- - - - - - - -
_____

Number Sense

7. Tom has 7 dots.
Can he put the same
number of dots on
each flag?

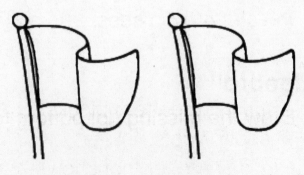

Yes   No

Problem Solving: Use Objects

John has 6 kites.
Use 6 pattern blocks
to show the kites.

Draw a picture to show the blocks.

Both ways show 6.

Use pattern blocks to model the problem.
Then draw a picture to show your blocks.

I. Marco has 4 baseballs.
Show the baseballs
Marco has.

2. Philip sees 8 stars
in the sky.
Finish drawing
the stars Philip sees.

Reasoning

3. Chris used pattern blocks
to show 7 cats.
Circle the letter that shows 7.

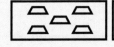   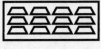

A   B   C

Problem Solving: Use Objects

Use counters to model the problem.
Then draw a picture to show your counters.

1. Alyssa bakes 6 cookies.
Show the cookies Alyssa bakes.

2. Farah buys 7 pens.
Show the pens Farah buys.

3. Eli puts away 5 hats.
Show the hats Eli puts away.

Journal

4. Write a problem for the picture.

_____

_____

_____

Comparing Two Numbers

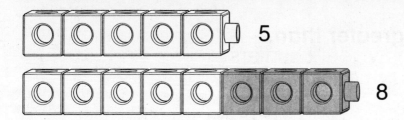

8 is more than 5.

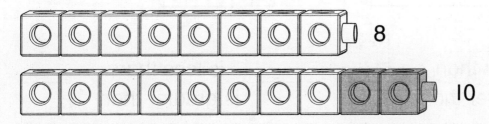

8 is fewer than 10.

Use cubes. Write the missing numbers. Circle **more** or **fewer**.

1.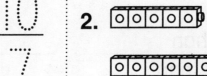

$\dot{1}\dot{0}$
$\underline{}$
7

more   fewer

10 is _____ than 7.

2.

5
_____

more   fewer

5 is _____ than 7.

3.

_____
_____

more   fewer

5 is _____ than 3.

4.

_____
_____

more   fewer

10 is _____ than 8.

Comparing Two Numbers

Practice **2-1**

Write each number.

Circle **is less than** or **is greater than**.

1.

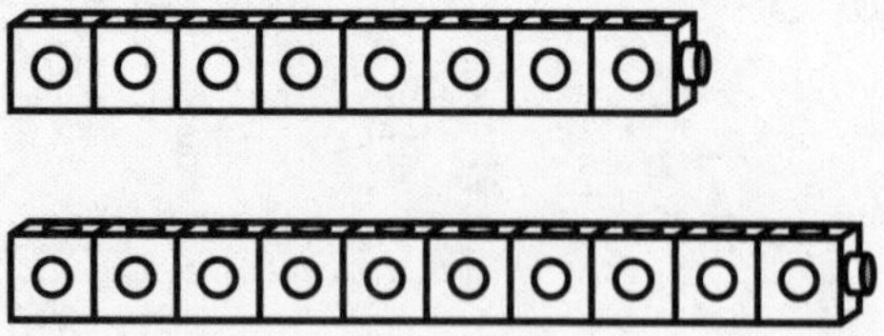

__8__ (is less than) __10__.
is greater than

2.

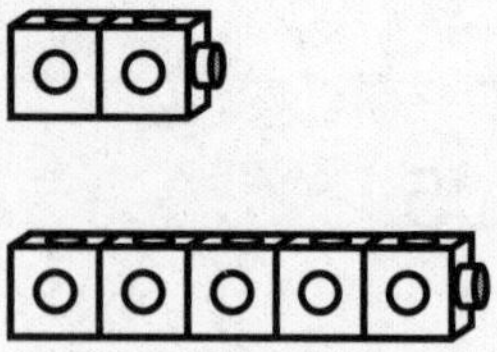

_____ is less than _____.
is greater than

3.

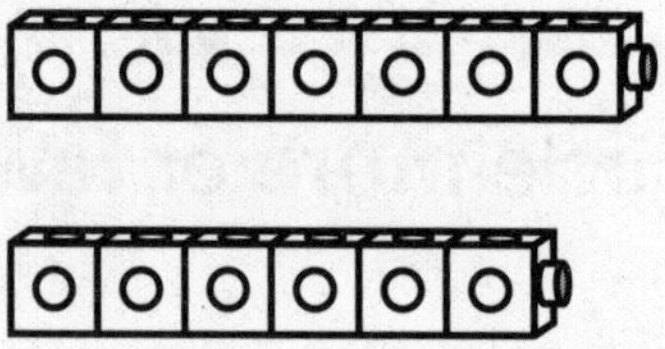

_____ is less than _____.
is greater than

4.

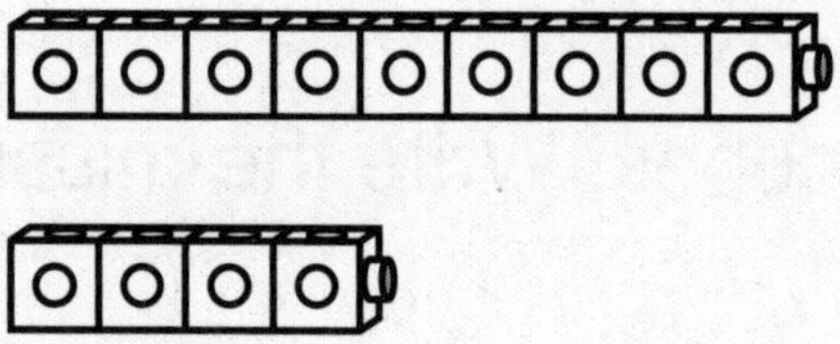

_____ is less than _____.
is greater than

Journal

5. Write a number
that is less than 10.
Draw a picture
to show that
many apples.

_____ apples

Ordering Three Numbers

You can put numbers in order.

2 is the least.

4 is between.

7 is the greatest.

> The numbers are in order from least to greatest.

Use cubes. Write the missing numbers.

1. 5

   3

   8

   _____ is the least.

   _____ is the greatest.

2. _____

   _____

   _____

   _____ is the least.

   _____ is the greatest.

3. _____

   _____

   _____

   _____ is the least.

   _____ is the greatest.

Ordering Three Numbers

Write the numbers in order from least to greatest.

1.

<u> 1 </u>	<u> 5 </u>	<u> 8 </u>
least	between	greatest

2. [4] [2]

___	___	___
least	between	greatest

3.

___	___	___
least	between	greatest

4. [4] [5] [1]

___	___	___
least	between	greatest

Number Sense

5. Which number is between 2 and 8?

(A) 1

(B) 6

(C) 9

(D) 11

Journal

6. Choose 3 numbers. Put your numbers in order from greatest to least.

Ordering Numbers to 12 with a Number Line

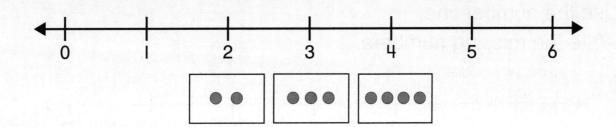

3 is **before** 4.

3 is one **after** 2.

3 is **between** 2 and 4.

Use the number line.
Write the number that is one before.

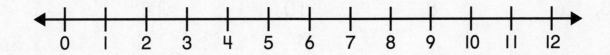

1. _____, 7

2. _____, 9

Write the number that is one after.

3. 6, _____

4. 8, _____

Write the number that is between.

5. 9, _____, 11

6. 10, _____, 12

Ordering Numbers to 12 with a Number Line

Use the number line.
Write the missing numbers.

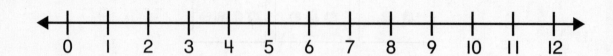

0 1 2 3 4 5 6 7 8 9 10 11 12

1. 3 4 ____ 6 7 8 ____

2. 2 3 ____ 5 ____ 7

3. 6 ____ 8 ____ 10 ____ 12

4. 4 ____ 6 7 ____ 9 ____

Number Sense

Use the clues. Mark the number.

5. My number is between 7 and 12.
It is after 9.
Which is my number?

6   8   9   10
Ⓐ   Ⓑ   Ⓒ   Ⓓ

Problem Solving: Act It Out

One way to solve a problem is to
use pattern blocks and act it out.

Marcie has 4 stickers.
Clyde has 2 stickers.
Bella has 6 stickers.

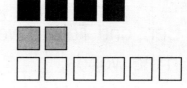

To find who has the most stickers,
put the blocks in order from
fewest to most.

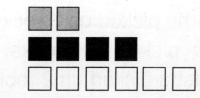

Write the numbers. __2__   __4__   __6__
                                 least between greatest

Who has the most stickers?_____Bella_____

Use blocks or counters to act out the story.
Put the numbers in order from least to greatest.

1. Kim has 6 buttons.
Max has 8 buttons.
Jane has 2 buttons.   __2__ ____ ____
                                       least between greatest

Who has the
most buttons?_____

2. Mike has 4 grapes.
Carla has 9 grapes.
Bob has 6 grapes.   ____ ____ ____
                                 least between greatest

Who has the
most grapes?_____

Problem Solving: Act It Out

Use cubes to act out the story.
Put the numbers in order from
least to greatest.

Harris, Ben, and Taisha went on
a walk in the woods.

1. Harris picked up 3 rocks.
   Ben picked up 7 rocks.
   Taisha picked up 2 rocks.

   _____ _____ _____
   least between greatest

   Who picked up the least number of rocks? _____

2. Then, Harris picked up 12 nuts.
   Ben picked up 1 nut.
   Taisha picked up 5 nuts.

   _____ _____ _____
   least between greatest

   Who picked up the greatest number of nuts? _____

3. Next, Harris picked up 11 leaves.
   Ben picked up 8 leaves.
   Taisha picked up 10 leaves.

   _____ _____ _____
   least between greatest

   Who picked up the least number of leaves? _____

Number Sense

4. Rob has 7 apples. Amanda has 4 apples.
   Meg has 10 apples.
   Which shows the number of apples from greatest to least?

   4, 7, 10   7, 10, 4   4, 10, 7   10, 7, 4
     Ⓐ   Ⓑ   Ⓒ   Ⓓ

© Pearson Education, Inc. 1

Practice 2-4

Making 6 and 7

You can use different ways to make 6.

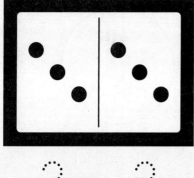

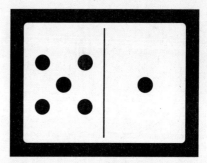

3 and 3

5 and 1

Write the numbers that show ways to make 6.

1.
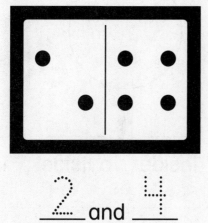

2 and 4

2.
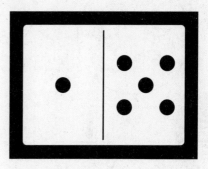

____ and ____

3.

____ and ____

4.
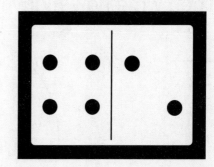

____ and ____

Making Parts of 6 and 7

Write the number inside and outside.
Then write the number in all.

1.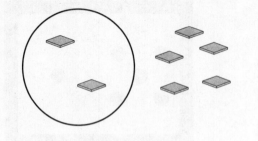

_____ _____ _____
inside   outside   in all

2.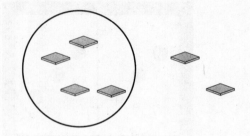

_____ _____ _____
inside   outside   in all

3.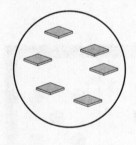

_____ _____ _____
inside   outside   in all

4.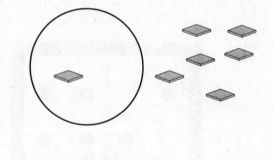

_____ _____ _____
inside   outside   in all

5. Draw 5 tiles inside the circle and 1 tile outside.
Then write how many in all.

_____

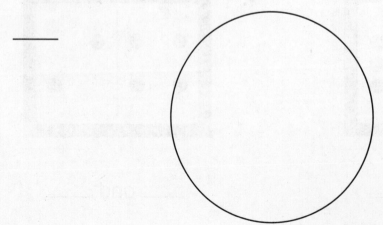

42 Topic 3

Name _____

Making 8

You can use different ways to make 8.

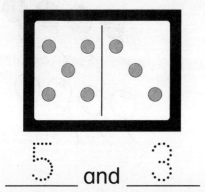

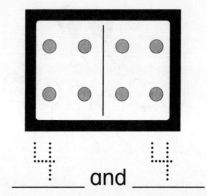

_5_ and _3_   _4_ and _4_

Write the numbers that show ways to make 8.

1.

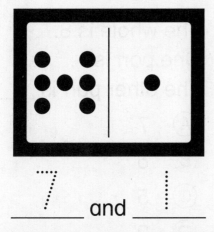

_7_ and _1_

2.

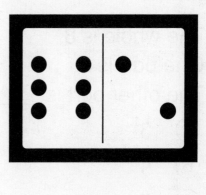

_____ and _____

3.

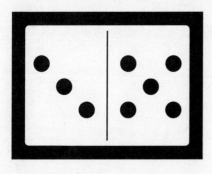

_____ and _____

4.

_____ and _____

Making 8

Write the numbers to show parts of 8.

1.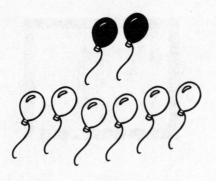

_____ and _____

2.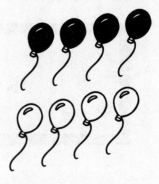

_____ and _____

Algebra

3. The whole is 8.
   One part is 3.
   The other part is _____.

   (A) 3
   (B) 4
   (C) 5
   (D) 8

4. The whole is 8.
   One part is 1.
   The other part is _____.

   (A) 7
   (B) 6
   (C) 5
   (D) 2

Journal

5. The whole is 8.
   One part is 8.
   What is the other part? _____
   Tell how you know.

   _____

   _____

Making 9

You can make 9 in different ways.

 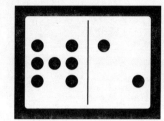 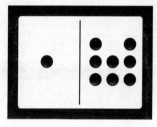

_3_ and _6_   _7_ and _2_   _1_ and _8_

Write the numbers that show ways to make 8 and 9.

1.
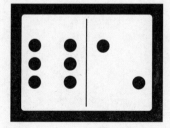

_3_ and _5_

___ and ___

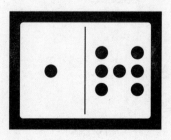

___ and ___

2.

___ and ___

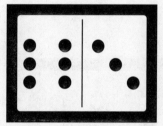

___ and ___

___ and ___

Making 9

Write the numbers to show parts of 9.

1.

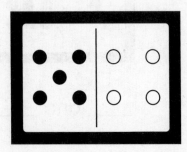

_____ ● and _____ ○

2.

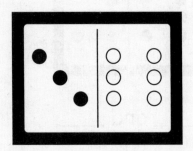

_____ ● and _____ ○

Visual Thinking

3. Which tells about the picture?

7 and 2	8 and 1	6 and 3	9 and 0
Ⓐ	Ⓑ	Ⓒ	Ⓓ

Introducing Addition Number Sentences

Join the parts to make the whole.

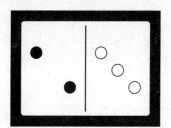

How many black counters? _____

How many white counters? _____

_2_ and _3_ is _5_ in all. 5 is the sum of 2 and 3.

Add to find the sum. Use counters if you like.

I.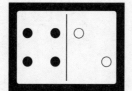

How many black counters? _____

How many white counters? _____

_4_ and _2_ is _6_ in all. 6 is the sum of 4 and 2.

2.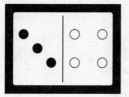

____ and ____ is ____ in all.

3.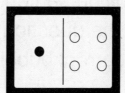

____ and ____ is ____ in all.

4.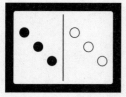

____ and ____ is ____ in all.

5.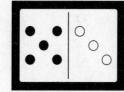

____ and ____ is ____ in all.

Introducing Addition Number Sentences

Use the picture. Write an addition sentence.

1.

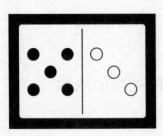

_____ + _____ = _____

2.

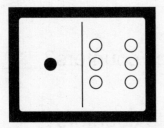

_____ + _____ = _____

Visual Thinking

3. Which addition sentence goes with the question? Fill in the correct bubble.

There are 4 brown rabbits in the garden.
There are 5 white rabbits.
How many rabbits are there in all?

Ⓐ $4 + 5 = 9$

Ⓑ $2 + 7 = 9$

Ⓒ $4 + 4 = 8$

Ⓓ $4 + 1 = 5$

Stories About Joining

Join the groups to find how many bugs in all.

Use a counter for each bug. Then count.

2 bugs are on the rock.

3 bugs are on the blanket.

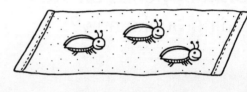

   I   2

3   4   5

How many bugs are there in all?   _____ bugs

Tell a joining story for each picture.
Use counters to tell how many in all.

I. 2 birds are in a tree.

2 birds are in a nest.

How many birds are there in all?   _____ birds

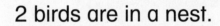

2. 3 fish are in a bowl.

2 fish are in another bowl.

How many fish are there in all?   _____ fish

Topic 3 **49**

Stories About Joining

Solve. Write an addition sentence.

1. 5 children are reading books.
Then 3 more children join them.

How many children are
reading books now?

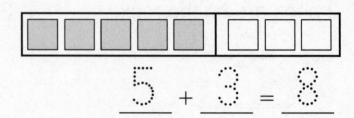

$$5 + 3 = 8$$

2. 7 children are running.
Then 2 more children join them.

How many children
are running now?

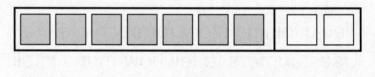

_____ + _____ = _____

3. 3 frogs are in the pond.
Then 3 more frogs join them.

How many frogs are in the
pond now?

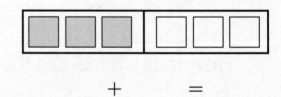

_____ + _____ = _____

Algebra

4. Which number makes the addition sentence true?

$$5 + \rule{2cm}{0.4pt} = 7$$

1	2	3	6
Ⓐ	Ⓑ	Ⓒ	Ⓓ

Adding in Any Order

You can add in any order and get the same sum.

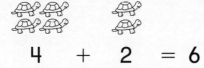
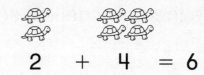

4 + 2 = 6   2 + 4 = 6

Add. Write an addition sentence with
the addends in a different order.

1.
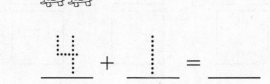

5 + 2 = 7   2 + 5 = 7

2.

4 + 1 = ___   ___ + ___ = ___

3.

___ + ___ = ___   ___ + ___ = ___

4.   5
       +4

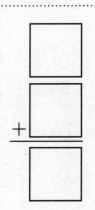

5.   3
       +4

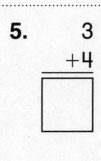

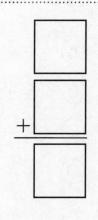

Adding in Any Order

Write the sum.
Then change the order of the addends.
Write the new addition sentence.

1. 6 + 1 = ___

___ + ___ = ___

2. 5 + 4 = ___

___ + ___ = ___

3. 6 + 3 = ___

___ + ___ = ___

4.

7
+ 1
───
8

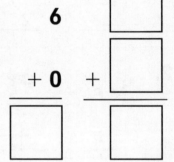

+ □
───
□

5.

7
+ 2
───
□

□
+ □
───
□

6.

6
+ 0
───
□

□
+ □
───
□

Algebra

7. Which is the same
as 5 + 1?

Ⓐ 1 + 2

Ⓑ 5 + 3

Ⓒ 2 + 6

Ⓓ 1 + 5

8. Which is the same
as 4 + 3?

Ⓐ 3 + 2

Ⓑ 5 + 4

Ⓒ 3 + 4

Ⓓ 7 + 2

Problem Solving: Use Objects

You can use objects to help you solve problems.

Left   **Right**

Bert has 3 pennies.
He put them in 2 pockets.
Use cubes to show the
different ways Bert can do this.

List the different ways.

Right Pocket	0	I	2	3
Left Pocket	3	2	I	0

Use cubes to help you list the different ways.

I. Marlene has 6 grapes.
She puts them in 2 bowls.

Bowl I	0	I	2	3	4	5	6
Bowl 2	6						0

2. Keith has 7 model airplanes.
He wants to paint some white and some black.

Black	0							7
White	7							0

Problem Solving: Use Objects

Use counters to solve.

1. Lisa puts 8 sweaters into two drawers.
   What are two different ways she can do this?

2. Jack puts 7 plates on two tables.
   What are two different ways he can do this?

Number Sense

3. Lynn is planting 9 flowers
   in two boxes.
   She plants 6 in the first box.
   Which shows how many she
   plants in the second box?

Ⓐ   Ⓑ   Ⓒ   Ⓓ

Finding Missing Parts of 6 and 7

You can draw a picture to help you
find missing parts of 6 or 7.
Color the part you know.
Count the circles you did not color.
These circles are the missing part.
Write the number.

$2 + \underline{\hspace{1cm}} = 6$

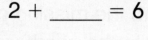

Whole

$2 + \underline{4} = 6$

Draw a picture to solve. Write the number.

1. Danielle has 6 toy trucks and cars.
   1 toy is a truck.
   How many toys are cars?

   $1 + \underline{5} = 6$

   ....

2. There are 7 cats in all.
   Some are black and some are white.
   3 cats are black.
   How many cats are white?

   $3 + \underline{\hspace{1cm}} = 7$

   ....

Reasoning

3. There are 6 ducks in the park.
   Some ducks are in the water.
   The same number are in the grass.
   How many ducks are in the grass?

   $\underline{\hspace{1cm}} + \underline{\hspace{1cm}} = 6$

Finding Missing Parts of 6 and 7

Find the missing part.
Write the numbers.

1.

_____   _____   _____
whole   part I know   missing part

2.

_____   _____   _____
whole   part I know   missing part

Journal

3. Draw a picture to solve.
   Write the number.
   There are 7 crackers in all.
   Melinda eats 2 crackers.
   How many crackers are left
   on the plate?

_____ crackers

Name_____

Finding Missing Parts of 8

You can draw a picture
to help you find missing parts of 8.
Color the part you know.
Count the circles you did not color.
These circles are the missing part.
Write the number.

$7 +$ ____ $= 8$

Whole

$7 + \underline{1} = 8$

Draw a picture to solve.
Write the number.

1. There are 6 penguins.
   2 penguins are small.
   How many penguins are big?

   $2 + \underline{4} = 6$

2. Andre has 8 puppies.
   Some puppies are in the house.
   4 puppies are playing in the yard.
   How many puppies are in the house?

   $4 +$ ____ $= 8$

Reasoning

3. Use the picture to solve.
   There are 8 marbles in all.

   _____ marbles are inside.

   _____ marbles are outside.   _____ $+$ _____ $= 8$

Finding Missing Parts of 8

1. Find the missing part.
Write the numbers.
There are 8 counters in all.

_____   _____
part I know   missing part

2. There are 8 counters in all.

_____   _____
part I know   missing part

Algebra

3. There are 8 books in all.
Which number sentence tells about the picture?

Ⓐ $8 - 1 = 7$

Ⓑ $8 - 2 = 6$

Ⓒ $8 - 3 = 5$

Ⓓ $8 - 4 = 4$

Finding Missing Parts of 9

You can draw a picture
to help you find missing parts of 9.
Color the part you know.
Count the circles you did not color.
These circles are the missing part.
Write the number.

$6 +$ _____ $= 9$

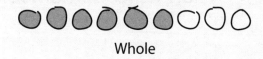

Whole

$6 +$ 3 $= 9$

Draw a picture to solve. Write the number.

1. There are 9 horses in the field.
8 horses are big. The rest are small.
How many horses are small?

$8 +$ _____ $= 9$

2. Alexis sees 9 frogs.
Some frogs are on a log.
2 frogs are in the grass.
How many frogs are on the log?

$2 +$ _____ $= 9$

Reasoning

3. Sam has 9 balloons.
He has one more red balloon
than he has blue balloons.
Write the number sentence.

_____ $+$ _____ $= 9$

Finding Missing Parts of 9

1. Find the missing part.
Complete the model.
Then write the numbers.

_____   _____
part I know   missing part

---

2. Maria sees 9 boats.
7 boats are in the water.
How many boats are not
in the water?

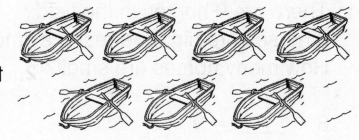

_____ boats

Journal

3. There are 9 apples in all.
Draw some on the tree.
Draw the rest of the apples
on the ground.

Write the numbers.

_____ apples on the tree

_____ apples on the ground

Introducing Subtraction Number Sentences

You can write a subtraction sentence to find how many are left.

___5___ take away ___2___ is ___3___.

___5___ minus ___2___ equals ___3___.

5   –   2   =   3

This is a subtraction sentence.

I.

4 minus I equals ___3___.

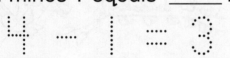

2.

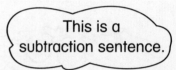

7 minus 4 equals _____.

Journal

3. Draw a picture that shows subtraction.

Write a subtraction sentence that tells about your picture.

Introducing Subtraction Number Sentences

Write a subtraction sentence.

1.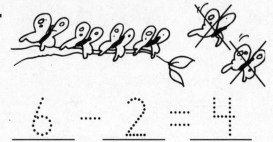

$6 - 2 = 4$

2.

$\underset{\_\_\_}{....} \underset{\_\_\_}{:::}$

3.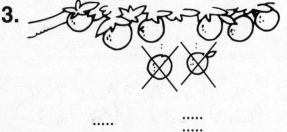

$\underset{\_\_\_}{....} \underset{\_\_\_}{:::}$

4.

$\underset{\_\_\_}{....} \underset{\_\_\_}{....}$

5.

$\underset{\_\_\_}{....} \underset{\_\_\_}{:::}$

6.

$\underset{\_\_\_}{....} \underset{\_\_\_}{....}$

Number Sense

7. Draw the missing dots.
Which subtraction sentence
tells about the model?

Ⓐ $9 - 2 = 7$
Ⓑ $9 - 5 = 4$
Ⓒ $9 - 6 = 3$
Ⓓ $5 - 4 = 1$

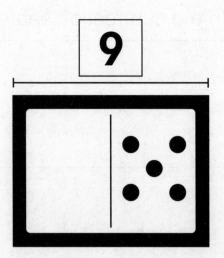

Name_____

Stories About Separating

There are 6 birds on the branch.
4 birds fly away.
How many birds are left?

You need to find how many birds are left.
Write a subtraction sentence to find
how many birds are left.

6 — 4 = 2

Check to see if your answer makes sense.

Write a subtraction sentence to answer
each question.

1. There are 8 marbles
in the bag.
3 marbles roll out.
How many marbles
are left in the bag?

____ ___ ____

2. Mary has 10 pencils.
She gives 4 pencils to Jack.
How many pencils does
Mary have left?

____ ___ ____

Stories About Separating

Use counters to answer each question.

1.

There are 5 children at the table.
3 children are eating.
How many children are not eating? ☐ children

2.

A man has 7 balloons.
2 balloons fly away.
How many balloons does the man have now? ☐ balloons

Algebra

3. 8 girls are jumping rope.
6 girls leave to play hopscotch.
How many girls are still jumping rope?
Which subtraction sentence tells
about the story?

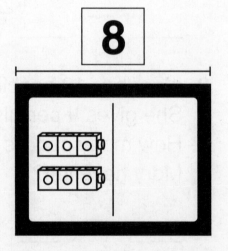

Ⓐ 8 − 1 = 7   Ⓒ 8 − 5 = 3

Ⓑ 8 − 2 = 6   Ⓓ 8 − 6 = 2

Stories About Comparing

Match the white cubes with the gray cubes.
Then count how many more.

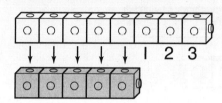

How many more
white cubes?   ⋰3⋱ more white cubes

How many fewer
gray cubes?   ⋰3⋱ fewer gray cubes

Write how many white cubes and how many gray cubes.
Then write how many more or how many fewer.

1.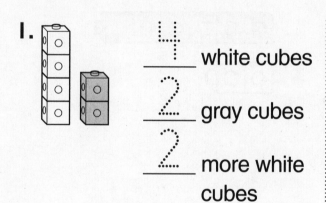

⋰4⋱ white cubes

⋰2⋱ gray cubes

⋰2⋱ more white cubes

2.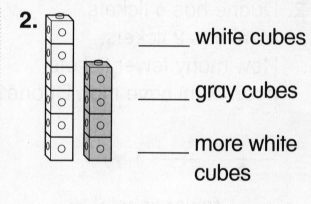

_____ white cubes

_____ gray cubes

_____ more white cubes

3.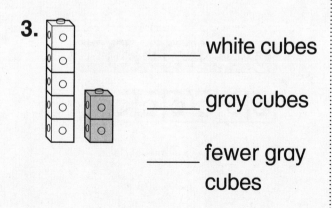

_____ white cubes

_____ gray cubes

_____ fewer gray cubes

4.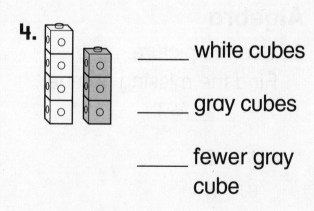

_____ white cubes

_____ gray cubes

_____ fewer gray cube

Stories About Comparing

Write a subtraction sentence.
Write how many more or fewer.

1. Sam sees 5 dogs.
Beth sees 3 dogs.
How many more dogs
does Sam see than Beth?

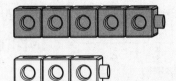

_____ − _____ = _____

_____ more dogs

2. Duane has 6 tickets.
Mimi has 2 tickets.
How many fewer tickets
does Mimi have than Duane?

_____ − _____ = _____

_____ fewer tickets

Algebra

3. Use the picture.
Find the missing number.
7 − _____ = 1

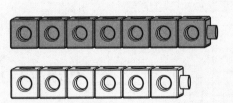

- Ⓐ 5
- Ⓑ 6
- Ⓒ 7
- Ⓓ 8

Connecting Addition and Subtraction

$4 + 3 = 7$

$7 - 3 = 4$

> The addition fact and the subtraction fact use the same numbers.

$6 + 4 = \underline{10}$

$\underline{10} - 4 = \underline{6}$

> The sum of the addition sentence is the first number in the subtraction sentence.

Write a related addition and subtraction sentence for each picture.

I.

$\underline{7} + \underline{4} = \underline{11}$

$\underline{11} - \underline{7} = \underline{4}$

2.

$\underline{} + \underline{2} = \underline{}$

$\underline{} - \underline{2} = \underline{}$

3.

$\underline{} + \underline{} = \underline{}$

$\underline{} - \underline{} = \underline{}$

4.

$\underline{} + \underline{} = \underline{}$

$\underline{} - \underline{} = \underline{}$

Connecting Addition and Subtraction

Write an addition sentence and a subtraction sentence for each picture.

1. ☐☐☐
☐☐☐☐☐☐☐

$\underline{3} + \underline{7} = \underline{10}$

$\underline{10} - \underline{3} = \underline{7}$

> The first number in the subtraction sentence is the sum of the numbers in the addition sentence.

2. △△△△△△△△
△

____ + ____ = ____

____ − ____ = ____

3. ☆☆
☆☆☆☆☆☆

____ + ____ = ____

____ − ____ = ____

Algebra

4. Which number is missing?

$4 + \underline{\hspace{1cm}} = 8$

- Ⓐ 2
- Ⓑ 3
- Ⓒ 4
- Ⓓ 5

5. Which number is missing?

$\underline{\hspace{1cm}} - 4 = 4$

- Ⓐ 8
- Ⓑ 7
- Ⓒ 6
- Ⓓ 4

Problem Solving: Use Objects

You can use objects
to show a story and
write a number sentence.

There are 6 hats.
Ashley takes 2 hats.

How many hats are left __4__?
Write the number sentence.

__6__ – __2__ = __4__

Cross out objects to show the story.
Write the number sentence.

1. There are 7 oranges.
   Jeff takes 3 oranges.
   How many oranges are left?

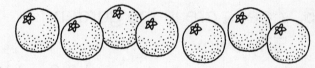

__7__ – ____ = ____

2. There are 5 airplanes.
   4 airplanes take off.
   How many airplanes
   are left?

____ – ____ = ____

Problem Solving: Use Objects

Use counters to show the story.
Write the number sentence.

1. 9 boys are at the park.
5 go home.
How many boys are left?

$$9 - 5 = 4$$

2. 6 ducks are in the pond.
3 fly away.
How many ducks are left?

____ – ____ = ____

3. There are 8 books on
the shelf.
Dana takes 2 books.
How many books are left?

____ – ____ = ____

4. There are 4 pears.
Emily eats 1.
How many pears are left?

____ – ____ = ____

5. 7 bees are in the garden.
5 fly away.
How many bees are left?

____ – ____ = ____

6. There are 3 block towers.
2 get knocked over.
How many towers are left?

____ – ____ = ____

Number Sense

7. You have 5 buttons.
Which is the greatest number of
buttons you can give away?

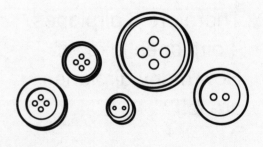

6   5   3 |
Ⓐ   Ⓑ   Ⓒ   Ⓓ

Representing Numbers on a Ten-Frame

You can use a ten-frame
to show numbers up to 10.

To show 3, start at the top left box.
Count as you draw a counter for
each number.

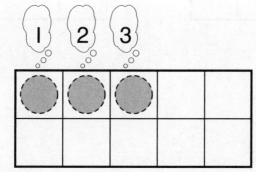

Draw counters in the ten-frame
to show each number.

1. 6

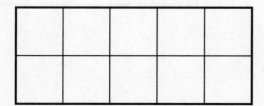

2. 8

3. 7

4. 9

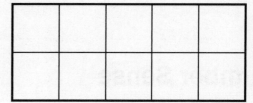

Representing Numbers on a Ten-Frame

Draw counters in the ten-frame to show each number.

1. $\boxed{4}$

2. $\boxed{6}$

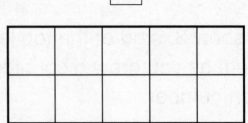

Algebra

Draw counters.

3. Show how 7 is 5 and 2.

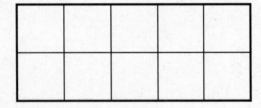

4. Show how 9 is 5 and 4.

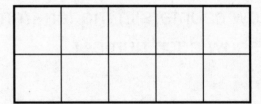

Number Sense

5. Kyle put 6 counters in a ten-frame. How many more counters should Kyle put in the frame to make 10?

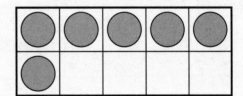

    (A) 2

    (B) 3

    (C) 4

    (D) 5

Recognizing Numbers on a Ten-Frame

A ten-frame is made up of 2 five-frames. So, you can use what you learned about five-frames to help you read numbers on a ten-frame.
For example, the number 8 on a five-frame and a ten-frame looks very much alike.

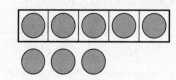

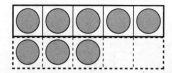

5 and 3 is 8.

Write the number shown on each ten-frame.

1. __7__

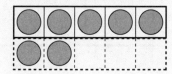

2. _____

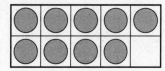

Spatial Thinking

Draw the counters.

3. Jim uses a ten-frame to show 5 and 5 more.

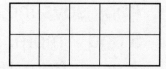

4. Bernice wrote about the ten-frame. Circle what Bernice wrote.

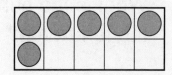

5 and 5 is 10.   4 away from 10 is 6.   5 and 2 is 7.

© Pearson Education, Inc. 1

Recognizing Numbers on a Ten-Frame

Write the number shown on each ten-frame.

1.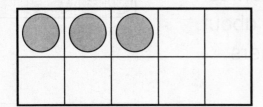

_____

2.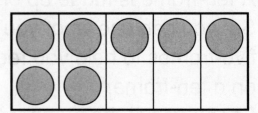

_____

Spatial Thinking

Draw the counters. Then write the number.

3. Rob uses a ten-frame.
He shows 5 and 3 more.
What number does he show?

_____

Number Sense

Draw the counters. Then solve the problem.

4. Abby says the ten-frame shows
5 and 2 more. Jake says it shows
3 away from 10.
What is the number in
the ten-frame?

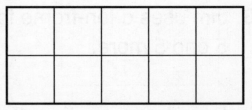

     7   5   3   2
    Ⓐ   Ⓑ   Ⓒ   Ⓓ

Parts of 10

Here are some different ways to make 10.

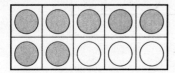

7 and 3

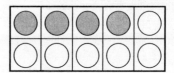

4 and 6

Write the numbers that show ways to make 10.

1.

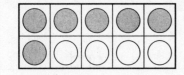

___6___ and ___4___

2.

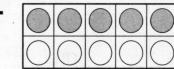

_____ and _____

3.

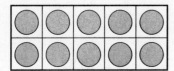

_____ and _____

4.

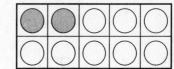

_____ and _____

5.

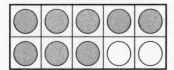

_____ and _____

6.

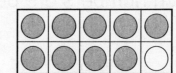

_____ and _____

Parts of 10

Write the numbers that show ways to make 10.

1.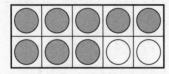

10 is ___8___ and ___2___

2.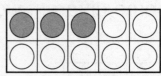

10 is _____ and _____

3.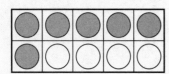

10 is _____ and _____

4.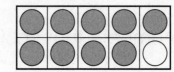

10 is _____ and _____

5.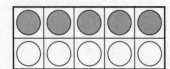

10 is _____ and _____

6.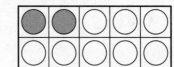

10 is _____ and _____

Number Sense

7. Which numbers are parts of 10?

Ⓐ 1 and 8

Ⓑ 4 and 5

Ⓒ 7 and 3

Ⓓ 9 and 2

Finding Missing Parts of 10

You can use a ten-frame
to help you find missing parts of 10.

Draw the counters from
the model in a ten-frame.
This is the part you know.

To find the missing part,
draw more counters to fill the frame.

Write the numbers.

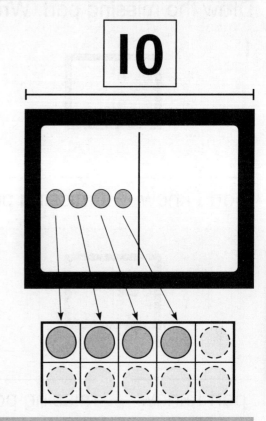

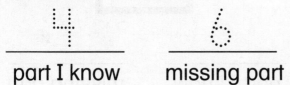

part I know   missing part

1. Look at the model.
   Draw the missing part in the ten-frame.
   Write the numbers.

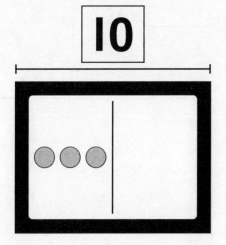

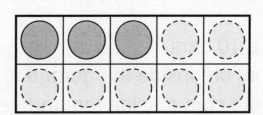

_____   _____
part I know   missing part

Finding Missing Parts of 10

Draw the missing part. Write the numbers.

1.

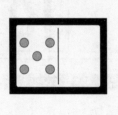

_____ 5 _____   _____ 5 _____
part I know   missing part

2.

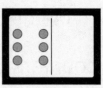

_____   _____
part I know   missing part

3.

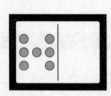

_____   _____
part I know   missing part

4.

_____   _____
part I know   missing part

Algebra

Write the missing part.

5. $4 +$ _____ $= 10$

6. $1 +$ _____ $= 10$

Journal

Draw a picture to solve the problem.

7. There are 10 cars.
Some cars are inside the garage.
Draw some cars outside the garage.
Write the parts.

_____   _____
part I know   missing part

Problem Solving: Make a Table

Katrina has purple marbles and yellow marbles. She can only fit 5 marbles in her pocket. How many different ways can Katrina put 5 marbles in her pocket?

To solve the problem, you need to find how many different ways Katrina can put the marbles in her pocket.

You can make a table and then count how many ways you made.

1. Complete the table.

2. There are _____ different ways.

3. What is the sum of each row in your table?

_____

Purple Marbles	Yellow Marbles
5	0
4	1
3	2

Problem Solving: Make a Table

Make a table to solve the problem.

1. Ed eats 6 pieces of fruit.
   He can eat strawberries or grapes.

   Show the ways Ed could pick which fruit to eat.

   _____ ways

2. If Ed eats 4 strawberries,
   how many grapes does he eat?

   _____

Strawberries	Grapes
0	
	3
6	

Reasoning

3. Kathy has red balloons and
   blue balloons.
   She gives away 5 balloons.

   If she gives away 3 red balloons,
   how many blue balloons does
   she give away?

   Ⓐ 3
   Ⓑ 2
   Ⓒ 1
   Ⓓ 0

Red	Blue

Adding with 0, 1, 2

You can count on to add with 0, 1, and 2.

(3) + 2 = _____

Circle the greater number.

Start with the greater number.

Then count on to add.

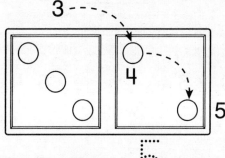

$3 + 2 = \underline{5}$

Circle the greater number. Count on to find each sum.

1.

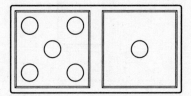

(5) + 1 = _6_

2.

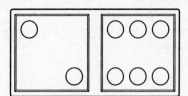

2 + (6) = _____

3.

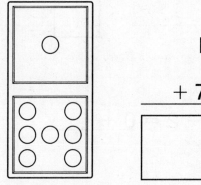

$\begin{array}{r} 1 \\ + 7 \\ \hline \end{array}$

4.

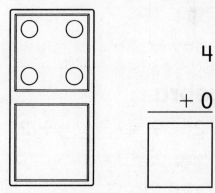

$\begin{array}{r} 4 \\ + 0 \\ \hline \end{array}$

Number Sense

5. 2 more than 7 is _____.

6. _____ more than 9 is 10.

Adding with 0, 1, 2

Write the sum.

1. 7 + 0 = _____

2. 1 + 6 = _____

3. 4 + 2 = _____

4. 0 + 5 = _____

5. 4 + 1 = _____

6. 1 + 1 = _____

7.
$$\begin{array}{r} 2 \\ + 7 \\ \hline \square \end{array}$$

8.
$$\begin{array}{r} 1 \\ + 8 \\ \hline \square \end{array}$$

9.
$$\begin{array}{r} 0 \\ + 9 \\ \hline \square \end{array}$$

10.
$$\begin{array}{r} 7 \\ + 0 \\ \hline \square \end{array}$$

11.
$$\begin{array}{r} 6 \\ + 1 \\ \hline \square \end{array}$$

12.
$$\begin{array}{r} 5 \\ + 2 \\ \hline \square \end{array}$$

Algebra

13. 2 + 9 = _____ + 2

- (A) 11
- (B) 10
- (C) 9
- (D) 2

14. 1 + 2 = 0 + _____

- (A) 1
- (B) 2
- (C) 3
- (D) 4

Name_____

Doubles

You can use a double to add.

Both addends
are the same.
They are doubles.

_2_ + _2_ = _4_   _3_ + _3_ = _6_

Write an addition sentence for each double.

1.

_4_ + _4_ = _8_

2.

_6_ + ____ = ____

3.

____ + ____ = ____

4.

____ + ____ = ____

5.

How many coins
are there in all?

____ + ____ = ____

6.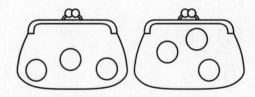

How many coins
are there in all?

____ + ____ = ____

Doubles

Write the sum.

1.   4
   + 4
   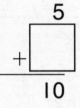

2.   6
   + ☐
   ‾‾‾‾
     12

3.   1
   + 1
   ‾‾‾‾
   ☐

4.   3
   + 3
   ‾‾‾‾
   ☐

5.   5
   + ☐
   ‾‾‾‾
     10

6.   0
   + 0
   ‾‾‾‾
   ☐

7.   2
   + 2
   ‾‾‾‾
   ☐

8.   7
   + 7
   ‾‾‾‾
   ☐

9. ☐ + ☐ = 16

10. ☐ + 9 = 18

Algebra

11. 1 + 1 + 2 + 2 = _____

(A) 3

(B) 4

(C) 5

(D) 6

Near Doubles

We can use doubles to add other numbers.

2 + 2

2 + 2 and 1 more

2 + 2 = 4   2 + 3 = 5

Find each sum. Use counters if you like.

1.

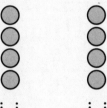

___ + ___ = ___   ___ + ___ = ___

2.

___ + ___ = ___   ___ + ___ = ___

Write a double or a double plus one for each sum.

3.

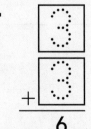

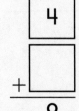

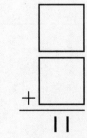

6   7   8   9   10   11

Near Doubles

Add.

1. 3
  + 2
  [5]

2. 3
  + 4
  [ ]

3. 1
  + 0
  [ ]

4. 4
  + 5
  [ ]

5. 1
  + [ ]
  ‾‾‾
  3

6. 5
  + [ ]
  ‾‾‾
  11

7. 4 + [ ] = 7

8. 5 = [ ] + 3

Journal

9. How does knowing the double 6 + 6 = 12
help you solve the near double 6 + 7 = 13?

_____

_____

_____

Facts with 5 on a Ten-Frame

You can use a ten-frame to learn facts with 5.
Look at the addition sentence.
Draw counters in the frame.

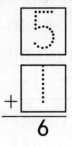

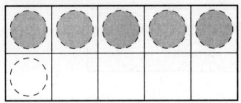

$5 + 1 = 6$

Draw counters and fill in the missing numbers.

1.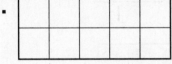

$5 + 2 = \underline{7}$

2.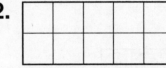

$4 + 5 = \underline{\hspace{1cm}}$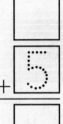

3.

$3 + 5 = \underline{\hspace{1cm}}$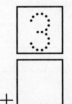

4.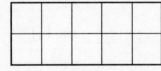

$5 + 0 = \underline{\hspace{1cm}}$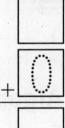

Number Sense

5. Nessa has 5 gray counters.
How many white counters does Nessa need
to have 10 counters in all?

10	9	6	5
Ⓐ	Ⓑ	Ⓒ	Ⓓ

Facts with 5 on a Ten-Frame

Look at the ten-frames.
Write an addition fact with 5.
Then write an addition fact for 10.

1.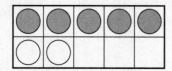

5 + _2_ = _7_

_7_ + _____ = 10

2.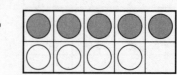

5 + _____ = _____

_____ + _____ = 10

3.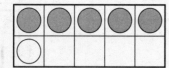

5 + _____ = _____

_____ + _____ = 10

4.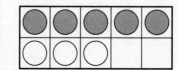

5 + _____ = _____

_____ + _____ = 10

Algebra

5. 15 + 2 = 17

17 + ____ = 20

Ⓐ 2
Ⓑ 3
Ⓒ 5
Ⓓ 17

6. 15 + 4 = 19

19 + ____ = 20

Ⓐ 15
Ⓑ 4
Ⓒ 2
Ⓓ 1

Making 10 on a Ten-Frame

You can make 10 to add.
Draw 7 white squares and
4 shaded squares.

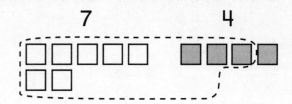

7   4

Circle a group of 10 squares.
Count the squares left over.
Then complete the number sentence.

_10_ + _1_ = 11, so 7 + 4 = 11

Circle a group of 10.
Write two addition sentences.

1. Hank has 9 black socks
and 3 white socks.
How many socks does
Hank have in all?

9   3

10 + _____ = 12, so 9 + 3 = _____

2. Pedro has 8 marbles in the
left pocket of his pants.
He has 7 marbles in the
right pocket.
How many marbles does
Pedro have in all?

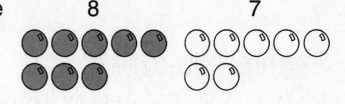

8   7

10 + _____ = _____, so 8 + 7 = _____

Making 10 on a Ten-Frame

Draw counters to solve. Write the missing numbers.

1.   8   10

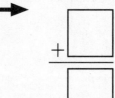
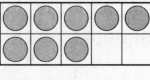

2.   9   10

3.   7   10

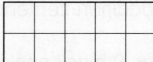

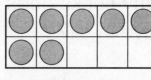
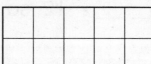

Journal

4. Draw a picture of 8 purple flowers
and 4 red flowers.
Draw a picture of 10 red squares
and 2 purple squares.
Write two addition sentences.

_____ + _____ = _____   _____ + _____ = _____

Problem Solving: Draw a Picture and Write a Number Sentence

There are 4 blue butttons.
There are 3 red buttons.
How many buttons are there?

You need to find how many buttons
there are in all.

Blue Buttons	Red Buttons
⊙	⊙
⊙	⊙
⊙	⊙
⊙	

You can draw a picture of the buttons.
Then you can write a number sentence.
Count the buttons in your picture to find the sum.

$$\underline{4} + \underline{3} = \underline{7}$$

4 + 3 = 7 buttons

Draw a picture.
Then write a number sentence.

I. Dan has 2 bird stamps.
He gets 4 cat stamps.
How many stamps
are there in all?

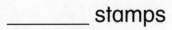

_____ stamps

_____ + _____ = _____

Reteaching 6-5

Problem Solving: Draw a Picture and Write a Number Sentence

Draw a picture. Write a number sentence.

1. Dean has 6 stamps.
   He gets 5 more stamps.
   How many stamps does
   he have in all?

   _____ + _____ = _____ stamps

2. Jan picks 8 red apples.
   Then she picks 4 yellow apples.
   How many apples does
   Jan pick in all?

   _____ + _____ = _____ apples

Number Sense

3. Which number sentence
   matches the picture?

    Ⓐ 5 − 4 = 1

    Ⓑ 4 + 5 = 9

    Ⓒ 3 + 6 = 9

    Ⓓ 5 + 5 = 10

Subtracting with 0, 1, and 2

You can count back to subtract 0, 1, or 2.

Remember when you subtract 2, think "2 less than."

4 − 2 = _____

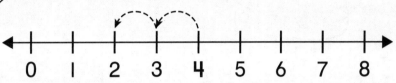

Start at 4.

Count back 2.

3, 2

Write the number.

4 − 2 = 2

Count back to subtract 0, 1, or 2.
Use a number line if you like.

1.

Count back 2.

5, _____

Write the number.

6 − 2 = _____

2.

Count back 1.

_____

Write the number.

9 − 1 = _____

3.

Count back 0.

_____

Write the number.

10 − 0 = _____

Subtracting with 0, 1, and 2

Count back to subtract. Use counters if you like.

1.

$$\begin{array}{r} 7 \\ -1 \\ \hline 6 \end{array}$$

Start at 7.
Count back 1.

2.
$$\begin{array}{r} 11 \\ -2 \\ \hline \end{array}\qquad \begin{array}{r} 6 \\ -1 \\ \hline \end{array}\qquad \begin{array}{r} 1 \\ -1 \\ \hline \end{array}\qquad \begin{array}{r} 7 \\ -0 \\ \hline \end{array}\qquad \begin{array}{r} 3 \\ -2 \\ \hline \end{array}\qquad \begin{array}{r} 12 \\ -1 \\ \hline \end{array}$$

3.
$$\begin{array}{r} 5 \\ -1 \\ \hline \end{array}\qquad \begin{array}{r} 10 \\ -2 \\ \hline \end{array}\qquad \begin{array}{r} 9 \\ -1 \\ \hline \end{array}\qquad \begin{array}{r} 3 \\ -1 \\ \hline \end{array}\qquad \begin{array}{r} 6 \\ -2 \\ \hline \end{array}\qquad \begin{array}{r} 10 \\ -1 \\ \hline \end{array}$$

4.
$$\begin{array}{r} 2 \\ -1 \\ \hline \end{array}\qquad \begin{array}{r} 4 \\ -0 \\ \hline \end{array}\qquad \begin{array}{r} 12 \\ -2 \\ \hline \end{array}\qquad \begin{array}{r} 8 \\ -2 \\ \hline \end{array}\qquad \begin{array}{r} 11 \\ -1 \\ \hline \end{array}\qquad \begin{array}{r} 9 \\ -2 \\ \hline \end{array}$$

Algebra

5. Three cats are asleep in a basket.
   If no cats wake up, which tells how many are asleep?

   (A) 0

   (B) 1

   (C) 2

   (D) 3

Journal

6. Draw a picture that shows 2 less than. Write a subtraction sentence for your story.

   _____ − _____ = _____

Thinking Addition

Doubles help you to subtract.

Think: 3 + 3 = __6__   so   6 - 3 = __3__

Add the doubles.
Then use the doubles to help you subtract.

1.

1 + 1 = __2__   so   2 - 1 = _____

2.

4 + 4 = _____   so   8 - 4 = _____

Visual Thinking

Complete the addition and subtraction sentences.

3. 2 + 2 = _____

4 - 2 = _____

Thinking Addition

Add the doubles.

Then use the doubles to help you subtract.

1.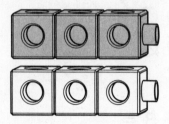

$$\begin{array}{r} 3 \\ + 3 \\ \hline 6 \end{array}$$

$$\begin{array}{r} 6 \\ - 3 \\ \hline 3 \end{array}$$

If $3 + 3 = 6$,
then $6 - 3 = 3$.

2.

$$\begin{array}{r} 4 \\ + 4 \\ \hline \end{array}$$

$$\begin{array}{r} 8 \\ - 4 \\ \hline \end{array}$$

3.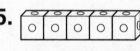

$$\begin{array}{r} 6 \\ + 6 \\ \hline \end{array}$$

$$\begin{array}{r} 12 \\ - 6 \\ \hline \end{array}$$

4.

$$\begin{array}{r} 2 \\ + 2 \\ \hline \end{array}$$

$$\begin{array}{r} 4 \\ - 2 \\ \hline \end{array}$$

5.

$$\begin{array}{r} 5 \\ + 5 \\ \hline \end{array}$$

$$\begin{array}{r} 10 \\ - 5 \\ \hline \end{array}$$

Number Sense

6. Mark the double that will help you subtract.

$8 - 4 =$ _____

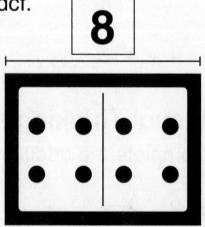

Ⓐ $3 + 3$

Ⓑ $4 + 4$

Ⓒ $5 + 5$

Ⓓ $8 + 8$

Thinking Addition to 8 to Subtract

You can think addition to help you subtract.

Think: I know
2 + 6 = 8,
so 8 – 6 = 2

2 + 6 = 8

8 – 6 = 2

Write an addition fact. Think of the addition fact to help you write and solve the subtraction fact.

1.

2 + 4 = 6

6 – 4 = 2

2.

___ + ___ = 7

7 – ___ = ___

3.

___ + ___ = ___

___ – ___ = ___

4.

___ + ___ = ___

___ – ___ = ___

Algebra

5. If △ + ○ = ▢, then _____ – _____ = _____

Thinking Addition to 8 to Subtract

Think addition to help you subtract.

1.

6

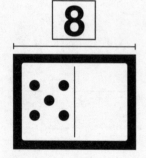

Think 4 + _____ = 6

so 6 – 4 = _____

2.

6

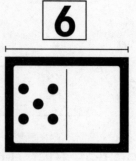

Think 5 + _____ = 6

so 6 – 5 = _____

3.

8

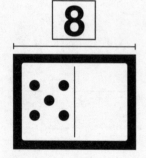

Think 5 + _____ = 8

so 8 – 5 = _____

4.

7

Think 4 + _____ = 7

so 7 – 4 = _____

Algebra

5. Tia needs to make 8 baskets. She makes 2 baskets.
How many more baskets does Tia need to make?
Which addition fact can help you subtract?

Ⓐ   8 + 6 = 14

Ⓑ   6 + 6 = 12

Ⓒ   2 + 8 = 10

Ⓓ   2 + 6 = 8

Thinking Addition to 12 to Subtract

You can use addition facts to help you subtract.

$8 + 1 = 9$

$9 - 1 = 8$

> $8 + 1 = 9$ and $9 - 1 = 8$ are related facts.

Use the addition fact to help you subtract.

1. $10 - 2 = $ _____ $8 + 2 = 10$

2. $11 - 4 = $ _____ $7 + 4 = 11$

3. $12 - 9 = $ _____ $3 + 9 = 12$

4. $11 - 6 = $ _____ $5 + 6 = 11$

Thinking Addition to 12 to Subtract

Think addition to help you subtract.

1. | **11** |

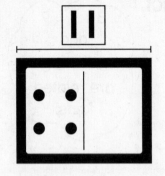

Think: 4 + _____ = 11

so 11 − 4 = _____

2. | **12** |

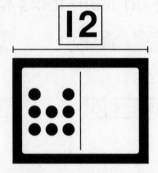

Think: 8 + _____ = 12

so 12 − 8 = _____

3. | **12** |

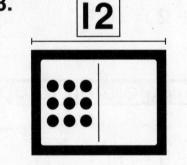

Think: 9 + _____ = 12

so 12 − 9 = _____

4. | **10** |

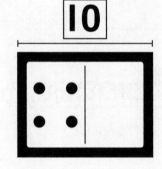

Think: 4 + _____ = 10

so 10 − 4 = _____

Problem Solving

5. Mark scores 6 points. Amy scores 11 points.
   How many points does Mark need to tie the game?
   Write a number sentence to solve.

   _____ ◯ _____ = _____

   _____ points

Problem Solving: Draw a Picture and Write a Number Sentence

You can draw a picture to help you solve a problem.

Mia has 7 grapes.
First, draw a picture of all the grapes.

Mia eats 3 grapes.
Cross out the grapes she eats.

Count how many grapes are left. _____ grapes

Write a number sentence that tells about the picture.

____7____ – ____3____ = ____4____

Check your work.
Does the number sentence match the picture?

Read the problem. Draw a picture.
Then write a number sentence.

I. Jonah has 9 baseballs.
Sara has 4 baseballs.
How many more baseballs
does Jonah have than Sara?

_____ – _____ = _____

Problem Solving: Draw a Picture and Write a Number Sentence

Write a subtraction sentence to solve.
Draw a picture to check.

1. Abby has 8 apples.
She gives away 3 apples.
How many apples does
she have left?

_____ – _____ = _____

2. Maya has 9 pears.
3 pears are green.
The rest are yellow.
How many pears are yellow?

_____ – _____ = _____

Reasoning

3. There are 7 birds. 3 birds fly away.
How many birds are left?
Which number sentence can
help you find the answer?

Ⓐ $7 - 2 = 5$

Ⓑ $7 - 3 = 4$

Ⓒ $9 - 7 = 2$

Ⓓ $7 - 6 = 1$

Identifying Plane Shapes

Plane Shapes

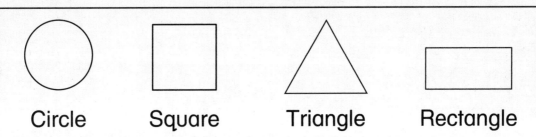

| Circle | Square | Triangle | Rectangle |

Color the shapes that are the same.
Circle its name.

1.

(square)

triangle

2.

square

circle

3.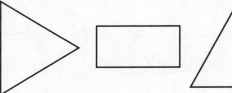

square

triangle

4.

rectangle

triangle

Identifying Plane Shapes

1. Draw a rectangle.

2. Draw a square.

3. Draw a triangle.

4. Draw a circle.

Geometry

5. I have 4 sides and 4 corners.
My sides are equal in length.
What shape am I?

Ⓐ   Ⓑ   Ⓒ   Ⓓ

Algebra

6. Which shape comes next in the pattern?

Ⓐ   Ⓑ   Ⓒ   Ⓓ

Properties of Plane Shapes

Count the straight sides.	Count the corners.	
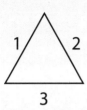	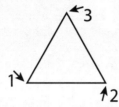	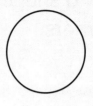
A triangle has straight sides.	A triangle has 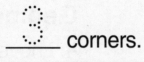 corners.	A circle has __0__ sides. A circle has __0__ corners.

1.

A square has __4__ straight sides.

A square has __4__ corners.

2.

A rectangle has _____ straight sides.

A rectangle has _____ corners.

3. Draw a shape with more than 4 corners.

4. Draw a shape with more than 4 straight sides.

Properties of Plane Shapes

1. Draw a shape with 4 corners.

2. Draw a shape with fewer than 4 straight sides.

3. Draw a shape with more than 4 straight sides.

Geometry

4. I have 4 equal sides and 4 corners.
What shape am I?

Ⓐ   circle

Ⓑ   square

Ⓒ   rectangle

Ⓓ   triangle

Reasoning

5. Here is the way Brian sorted some plane shapes.

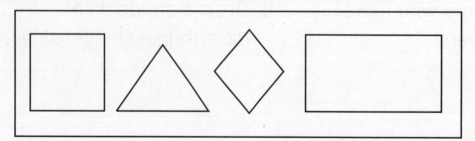

Circle the question Brian might have asked.

Does it have fewer than 5 corners?

Does it have more than 5 straight sides?

Making New Shapes from Shapes

Give 3 ways you can make this shape using pattern blocks.

You need to find all the ways that pattern blocks can make the shape.

A list can help you keep track.

Ways to Make ⬡			
Shapes I Used	⬡	△	▱
Way 1	1	0	0
Way 2	0	3	0
Way 3	0	1	1

Did you find 3 ways? How do you know?

Give 3 ways you can make this shape using pattern blocks. Complete the list.

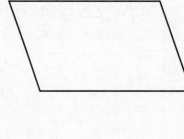

Ways to Make ▱			
Shapes I Used	⬡	▱	△
Way 1	1	0	1
Way 2			
Way 3			

Making New Shapes from Shapes

Use pattern blocks to make each shape.
Trace your new shape.

Use This Shape	Make This Shape	Trace New Shape
1.  △	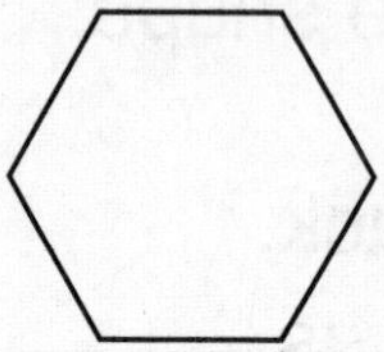 ⬡ (hexagon)	
2.  △	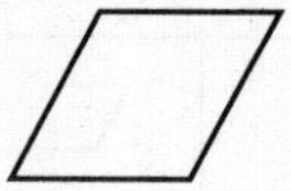 ▱ (parallelogram)	
3. 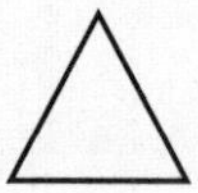 △	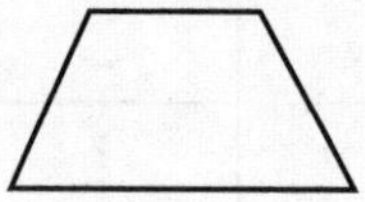 ⏢ (trapezoid)	

4. Mark the number that tells how
many △ you need to make a ⬡.

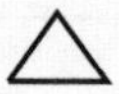

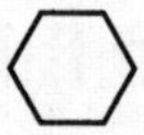

4
Ⓐ

5
Ⓑ

6
Ⓒ

7
Ⓓ

Journal

5. Use pattern blocks to make a new shape.
Trace the blocks you used below.

Breaking Apart Shapes to Make Shapes

You know you can use smaller
shapes to make a larger shape.

These 3 triangles can make
a trapezoid.

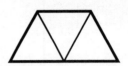

A larger shape can also break
apart to make smaller shapes.

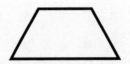

A trapezoid can make three
smaller triangles.

How many triangles can you make from each shape?
Draw lines.

1.

2.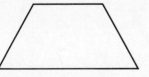

3.

4.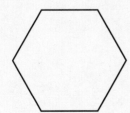

Breaking Apart Shapes to Make Shapes

1. Draw one line to make 2 triangles.

2. Draw one line to make 2 triangles.

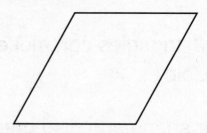

3. Draw 2 lines to make 3 triangles.

4. Draw 2 lines to make 3 rectangles.

Spatial Thinking

5. Which shows how to cut a rectangle into 4 triangles?

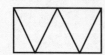

Ways to Move Shapes

Shapes can slide.	Shapes can flip.	Shapes can turn.
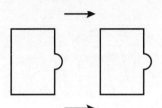	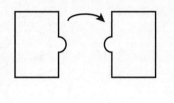	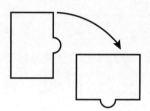

Is it a **slide**, a **flip**, or a **turn**?
Circle the answer.

1.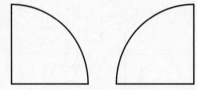

slide   (flip)   turn

2.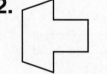

slide   flip   turn

3.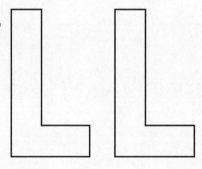

slide   flip   turn

4.

slide   flip   turn

Ways to Move Shapes

Is it a **slide**, a **flip**, or a **turn**?
Circle the answer.

1.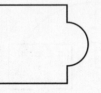

slide   (flip)   turn

2.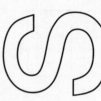

slide   flip   turn

3.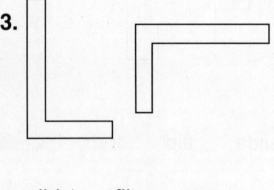

slide   flip   turn

4.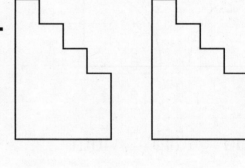

slide   flip   turn

Journal

5. Draw 3 different shapes that will all look the same after they are turned.

Practice 8-5

Name_____

Congruence

These rectangles are the same shape.

The rectangles are the same size.
Count the dots to make sure.

These rectangles are the same shape.

The rectangles are **not** the same size.
Count the dots to make sure.

Look at the first shape.
Then color the shape that matches it.

1.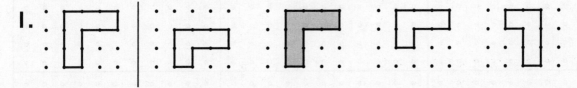

2.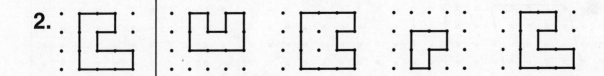

3.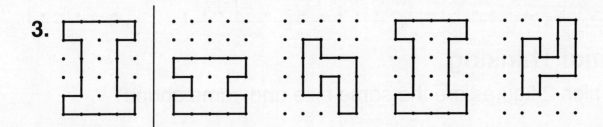

4.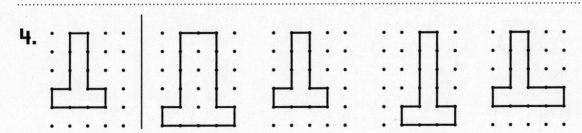

Congruence

Look at the first shape.
Draw one that matches it.
Then draw the shape in a different size.

Shape	Matching Shape	Different Size
I.		
2. 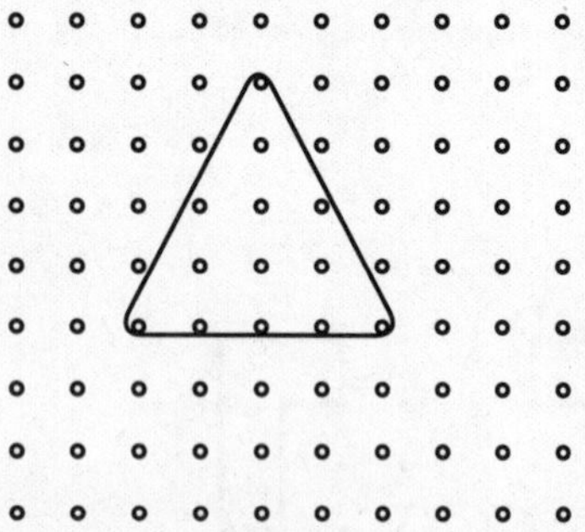		
3. 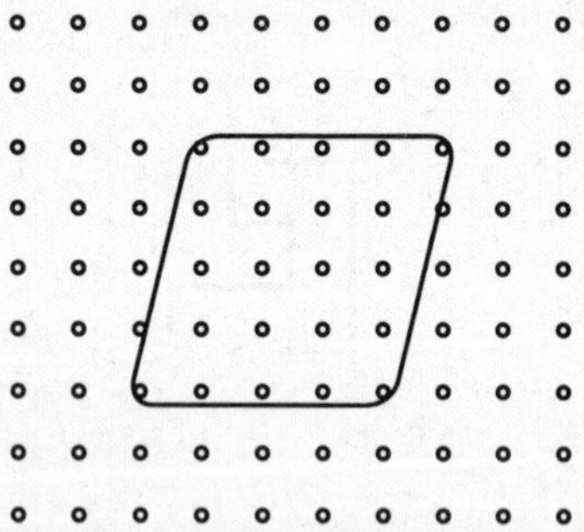		

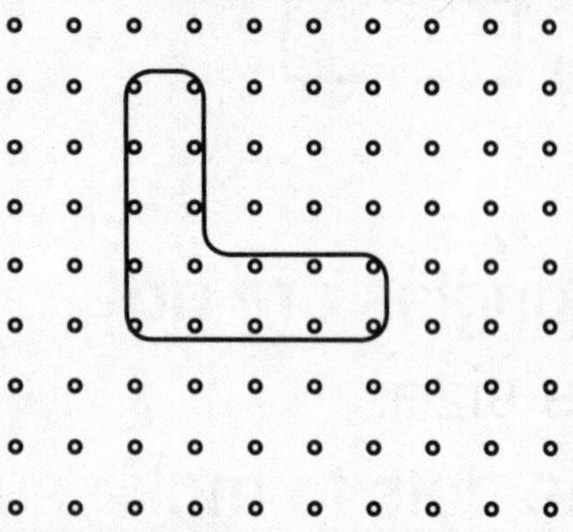

Spatial Thinking

4. Which 2 figures are the same size and same shape?

(A) ▢ ▢

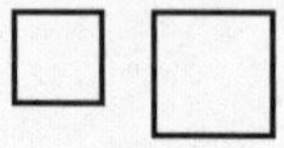

(B) ◯ ◯

(C) ◺ ◸

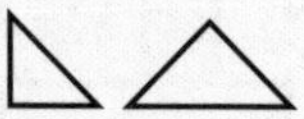

(D) ▯ ▭

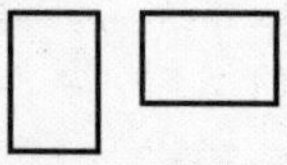

Symmetry

A line of symmetry separates a shape into 2 matching parts.

These 2 parts match.   These 2 parts do not match.

Color the shape that has 2 matching parts.

1.  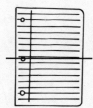   **2.**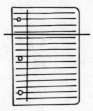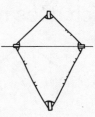

3. 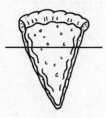    **4.**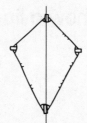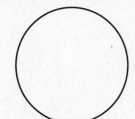

Visual Thinking

5. Draw a different line of symmetry on each circle.

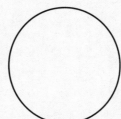 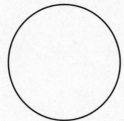 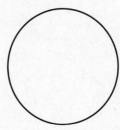

Symmetry

Draw a **line of symmetry** to make two matching parts.

1.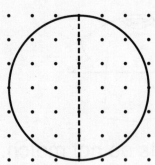

2.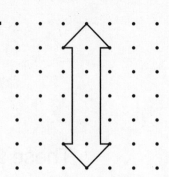

3.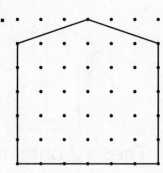

4.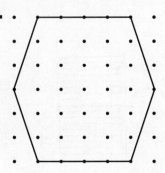

5.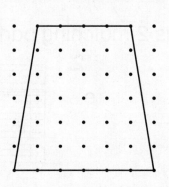

6.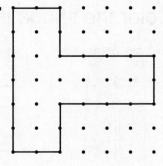

7. Which does not show a line of symmetry on the shape?

Ⓐ

Ⓑ

Ⓒ

Ⓓ

Problem Solving:
Make an Organized List

You can use pattern blocks to make another shape.

How many can fit in ? __2__

How many can fit in 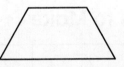 ? __3__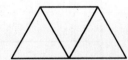

There are 3 ways you can make this shape using pattern blocks.

Complete the organized list.

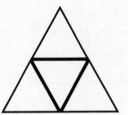

Ways to Make △			
	△	▱	⬜
Way 1	4	0	0
Way 2			
Way 3			

Problem Solving:
Make an Organized List

How many ways can you make
this shape using pattern blocks?

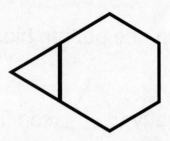

1. Make a list.

Ways to Make 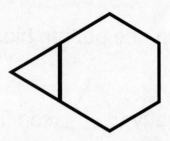				
Shapes I Used	⬜	⬡	△	▱
Way 1				
Way 2				
Way 3				
Way 4				
Way 5				
Way 6				

Journal

2. How many ways can you use pattern blocks
to make a ▱ ? Explain.

Identifying Solid Figures

These shapes are solid figures.

Sphere   Cone   Cylinder   Cube   Rectangular Prism

Color the spheres red. Color the cones blue.
Color the cylinders green. Color the cubes orange.
Color the rectangular prisms yellow.

I.

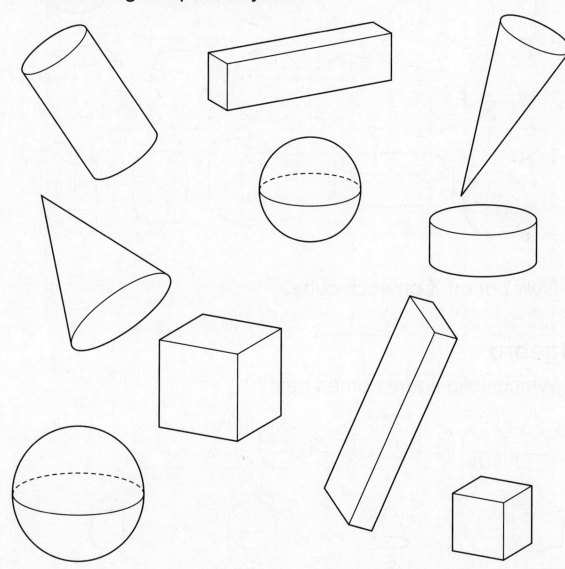

Identifying Solid Figures

1. Color each solid figure below.

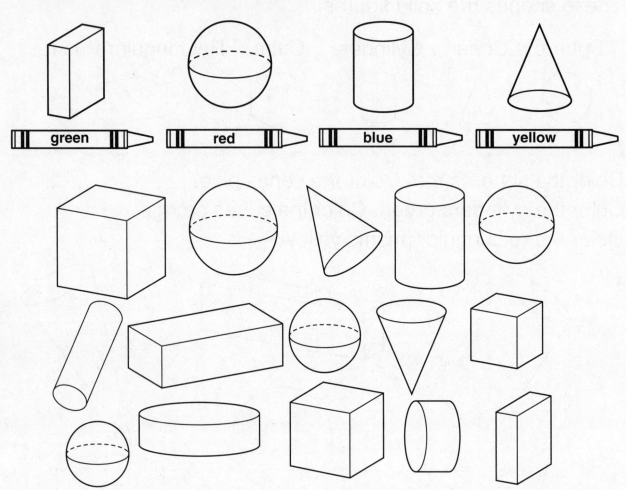

green   red   blue   yellow

2. Now put an X on each cube.

Algebra

3. Which solid figure comes next?

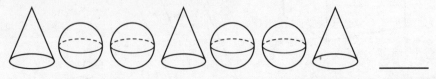

Ⓐ

Ⓑ

Ⓒ

Ⓓ

Practice 8-9

Flat Surfaces and Corners

These solid figures have **flat surfaces.**

 Cone   Cylinder

 Rectangular Prism   Cube

These solid figures have **vertices** or corners.

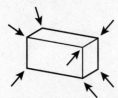   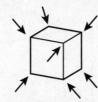

Use solid figures to complete the table.

Solid Figure	Number of Flat Surfaces	Number of Vertices (Corners)
1. cube	6	8
2. cone		
3. rectangular prism		
4. cylinder		

Flat Surfaces and Corners

Circle the solid figure that answers each question.

1. Which solid figure has 2 flat surfaces and 0 vertices?

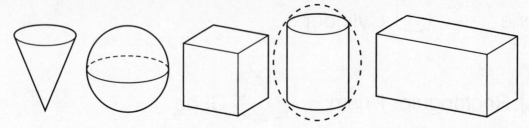

2. Which solid figure has 0 flat surfaces and 0 vertices?

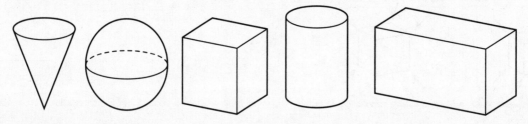

3. Which solid figures have 6 flat surfaces and 8 vertices?

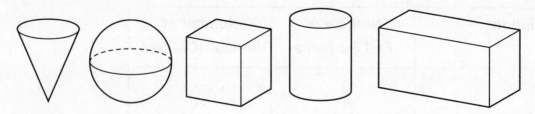

Reasoning

4. Mark the solid figure that answers the question.

I have 1 flat surface. I have 1 vertex.
Which solid figure am I?

   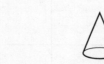

Ⓐ   Ⓑ   Ⓒ   Ⓓ

Sorting Solid Figures

You can sort solid figures in many ways.
Some figures can go into more than one group.

Some figures have flat
surfaces and cannot roll.

Some have flat surfaces
and can roll.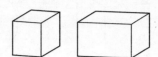

Some have vertices (corners).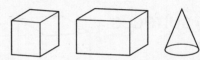

Some have no vertices (corners).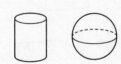

Circle the figure that follows the sorting rule.

1. It has all flat surfaces.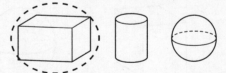

2. It has no flat surfaces.

3. It can roll.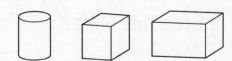

4. Circle the 2 figures
that have flat surfaces
and curves.

Sorting Solid Figures

Read the sorting rule.
Circle 1, 2, or 3 solid figures that follow the rule.

1. 1 flat surface

2. 8 vertices

3. 2 flat surfaces

4. 6 flat surfaces

5. 0 vertices

Algebra

6. Mark the rule that tells how these solid figures are alike.

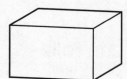

(A) 3 vertices

(B) 4 flat surfaces

(C) 5 vertices

(D) 6 flat surfaces

Describing Patterns

This is a pattern.

  repeats over and over.

This is a pattern too.

 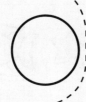   repeats over and over.

Circle the pattern unit.

1.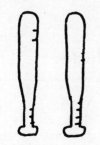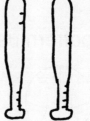

2.

3.

Describing Patterns

Circle the pattern unit.

1.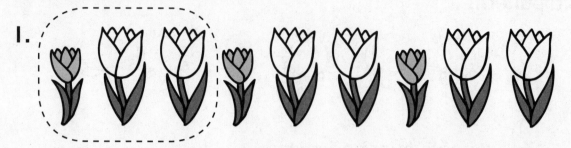

2.

3.

4.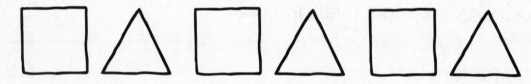

Journal

5. Make the same pattern using other shapes or letters.

Using Patterns to Predict

The stripes make a pattern.
What color should the white stripe be?

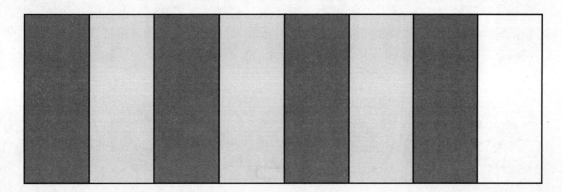

Find the pattern.
Color what is missing.

1.

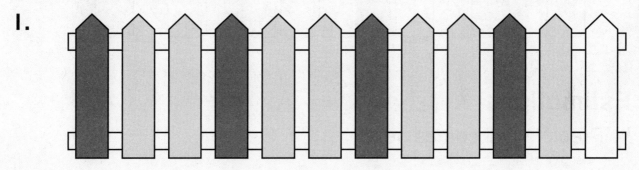

....

2.

Using Patterns to Predict

Find the pattern.
Circle what comes next.

1.

2.

3.

Estimation

4. Predict what comes next.

Ⓐ

Ⓑ

Ⓒ

Ⓓ

Extending Shape Patterns

Look at these patterns.

A   B   A   B   A   B

repeats over and over. A B repeats over and over.

Use pattern blocks. Make a pattern. Draw the pattern.
Then make the same pattern using letters.

1.

A   B   A   B   A   B
___ ___ ___ ___ ___ ___

2.

S T ___ ___ ___ ___ ___
___ ___ ___ ___ ___ ___ ___

Reasoning

3. Draw a picture that shows the part that repeats.

Extending Shape Patterns

Look at the pattern.
Make the same pattern using letters.

1.

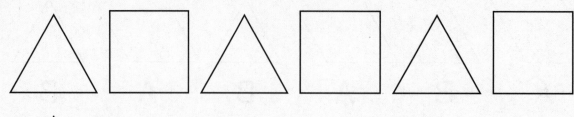

A __ __ __ __ __

....

2.

A __ __ __ __ __ __

....

Reasoning

3. Draw a picture that shows the part that repeats.

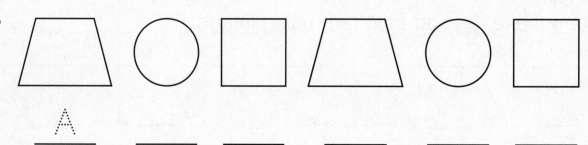

Problem Solving:
Look for a Pattern

A pattern can be anything that repeats.
It can be colors, shapes, numbers, letters,
or objects.
To find a pattern, look for what repeats.

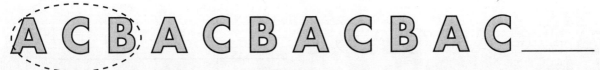

Write what comes next.

1. Zoë drew a pattern.

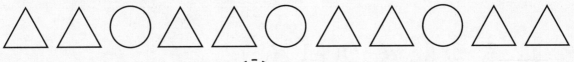

Draw what comes next.

Algebra

2. Use these shapes to make a pattern.

3. Use these numbers to make a pattern.

Problem Solving:
Look for a Pattern

Write, draw, or color to complete the pattern.

I. △ ○ ▭ △ ○ ▭ △ ○ ▭ _____ _____ _____

2. A D C A D C A D C _____ _____ _____

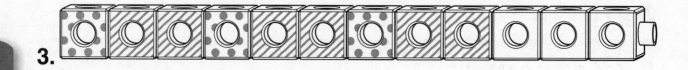

3.

4. 2 4 6 2 4 6 2 4 6 _____ _____ _____

Visual Thinking

5. Which ball is missing?

_____

A ●

B ◐★

C ●

D ●

Making Numbers 11 to 20

Write each number as 10 and some left over.

This shows 10.

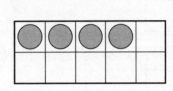

This shows 4 left over.

14 is ___10___ and ___4___.

1.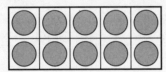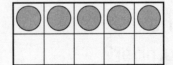

17 is ___10___ and ___7___.

2.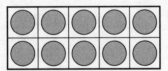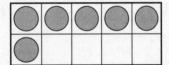

16 is _____ and ___6___.

3.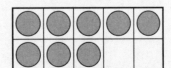

15 is _____ and _____.

4.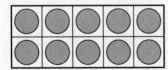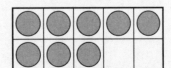

18 is _____ and _____.

Making Numbers 11 to 20

Write each number as 10 and some ones.

1. | twelve | 12 is __10__ and __2__.

2. | eighteen | 18 is _____ and _____.

3. | fourteen | 14 is _____ and _____.

4. | eleven | 11 is _____ and _____.

5. | seventeen | 17 is _____ and _____.

6. | nineteen | 19 is _____ and _____.

7. | sixteen | 16 is _____ and _____.

Algebra

8. Which is the missing number?

   13 is 10 and _____.

   Ⓐ   1
   Ⓑ   2
   Ⓒ   3
   Ⓓ   10

9. Which is the missing number?

   15 is _____ and 5.

   Ⓐ   10
   Ⓑ   5
   Ⓒ   3
   Ⓓ   1

Using Numbers 11 to 20

This shows 12.

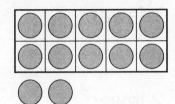

Count 10, 11, 12.

This shows **2 more** than 12.

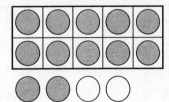

Count 10, 11, 12, 13, 14.
2 more than 12 is 14.

This shows 13.

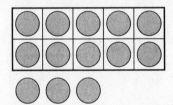

Count 10, 11, 12, 13.

This shows **2 fewer** than 13.

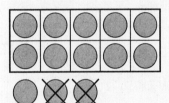

Count 10, 11.
2 fewer than 13 is 11.

Write the numbers.

1.

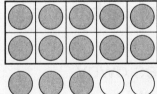

2 more than 13 is _15_.

2.

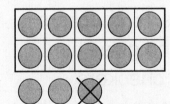

1 fewer than 13 is _____.

3.

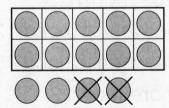

2 fewer than 14 is _____.

4.

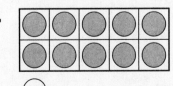

1 more than 10 is _____.

Using Numbers 11 to 20

Write the numbers.

1. twelve _____   1 more _____   1 fewer _____

2. seventeen _____   2 more _____   2 fewer _____

3. fifteen _____   2 more _____   2 fewer _____

4. nineteen _____   1 more _____   1 fewer _____

5. thirteen _____   2 more _____   2 fewer _____

Number Sense

6. Jeff has 16 checkers.
His friend gives him
2 more checkers.
Which number tells how
many checkers he has now?

Ⓐ 14
Ⓑ 15
Ⓒ 17
Ⓓ 18

Reasonableness

7. There are 12 birds in
the tree.
1 bird flies away.
Which tells how many
birds are left in the tree?

Ⓐ less than 10
Ⓑ between 10 and 12
Ⓒ between 12 and 15
Ⓓ more than 12

Counting by 10s to 100

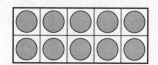 stands for one group of ten.

10, ten,	20, twenty,	30, thirty,	40, forty,	50, fifty,
60, sixty,	70, seventy,	80, eighty,	90, ninety,	100, one hundred

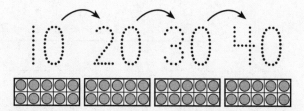

___4___ groups of ten

40 forty

Count by 10s. Then write the numbers.

1.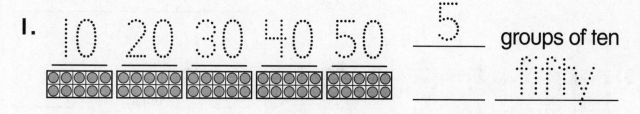

___5___ groups of ten

fifty

2.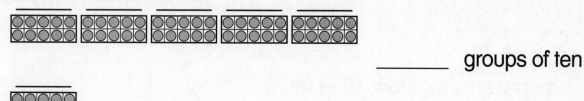

_____ groups of ten

_____ _____

3.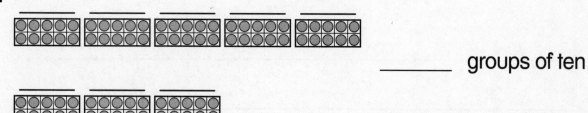

_____ groups of ten

_____ _____

Counting by 10s to 100

10, ten,	20, twenty,	30, thirty,	40, forty,	50, fifty,
60, sixty,	70, seventy,	80, eighty,	90, ninety,	100, one hundred

Count by tens. Then write the numbers.

1.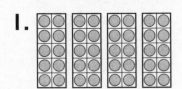

_____4_____ tens = ___40___

___forty___

2.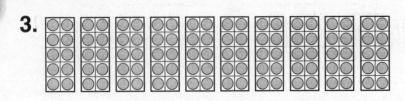

_____ tens = _____

_____

3.

_____ tens = _____

_____

Journal

4. Laura wants to show 70 in tens.
   How many tens will she draw?
   How do you know?

_____

_____

Counting Patterns on a Hundred Chart

Skip count by 10s on the hundred chart.

1	2	3	4	5	6	7	8	9	10	10
11	12	13	14	15	16	17	18	19	20	20
21	22	23	24	25	26	27	28	29	30	30
31	32	33	34	35	36	37	38	39	40	40
41	42	43	44	45	46	47	48	49	50	50
51	52	53	54	55	56	57	58	59	60	60
61	62	63	64	65	66	67	68	69	70	70
71	72	73	74	75	76	77	78	79	80	80
81	82	83	84	85	86	87	88	89	90	90
91	92	93	94	95	96	97	98	99	100	100

> When you skip count by 10s all of the numbers end in 0.

1. Skip count by 5s. Draw a square around the numbers you say.

2. When you skip count by 5s, all of the numbers end in

_____ or _____.

1	2	3	4	5	6	7	8	9	10
11	12	13	14	15	16	17	18	19	20
21	22	23	24	25	26	27	28	29	30
31	32	33	34	35	36	37	38	39	40
41	42	43	44	45	46	47	48	49	50
51	52	53	54	55	56	57	58	59	60
61	62	63	64	65	66	67	68	69	70
71	72	73	74	75	76	77	78	79	80
81	82	83	84	85	86	87	88	89	90
91	92	93	94	95	96	97	98	99	100

Counting Patterns on a Hundred Chart

1. Color the numbers you say when you count by 5s.

1	2	3	4	5	6	7	8	9	10
11	12	13	14	15	16	17	18	19	20
21	22	23	24	25	26	27	28	29	30
31	32	33	34	35	36	37	38	39	40
41	42	43	44	45	46	47	48	49	50
51	52	53	54	55	56	57	58	59	60
61	62	63	64	65	66	67	68	69	70
71	72	73	74	75	76	77	78	79	80
81	82	83	84	85	86	87	88	89	90
91	92	93	94	95	96	97	98	99	100

Continue the pattern. Write the numbers.

2. Count by 10s.

10, 20, 30, _____, _____, _____, _____, _____

3. Count by 2s.

2, 4, 6, _____, _____, _____, _____, _____

Reasoning

4. Write yes or no.
Vicki has baseball practice
every 5 days.
Will she have practice on
May 19? _____

May						
S	M	T	W	T	F	S
	1	2	3	4	5	6
7	8	9	10	11	12	13
14	15	16	17	18	19	20

Practice 10-4

Using Skip Counting

Skip count to find how many.

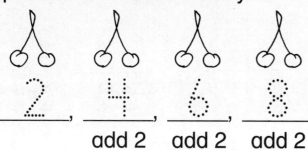

Skip count by 2, or add 2 to the last number.

___2___, ___4___, ___6___, ___8___
         add 2   add 2   add 2

There are ___8___ cherries.

---

1. Skip count by 2s.

___2___, ___4___, _____, _____, _____, _____

---

2. Skip count by 5s.

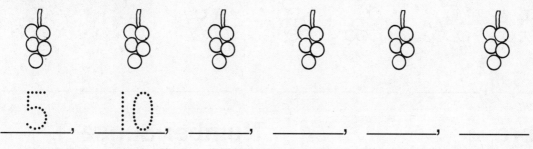

___5___, ___10___, _____, _____, _____, _____

---

3. Skip count by 10s.

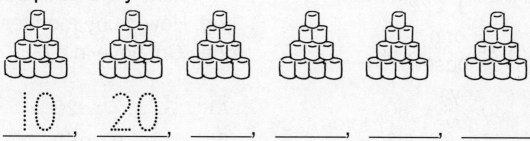

___10___, ___20___, _____, _____, _____, _____

Name_____

Using Skip Counting

Use the picture to skip count.

1. How many ears are there?
Count by twos.

_2_, _____, _____, _____, _____, _____, _____

2. How many cans are there?
Count by fives.

_____, _____, _____, _____, _____, _____, _____

3. How many balls are there?
Count by tens.

_____, _____, _____, _____, _____, _____, _____

Algebra

4. Look for a pattern.
Find the missing number.

75, 70, 65, 60, 55, 50, _____

 30   40
 35   45

Number Sense

5. Cal has 8 bags.
He puts 5 marbles in each
bag. How many marbles
does Cal have in all?

 3   20
 13   40

Practice 10-5

Odd and Even Numbers

6 is an even number.
It makes two equal rows.
There are no extras.

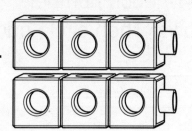

These cubes match.

7 is an odd number.
It does not make
two equal rows.
There is 1 extra.

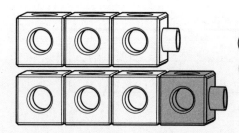

These cubes don't match.

Use cubes to show each number.
Try to make equal rows. Then circle odd or even.

1.

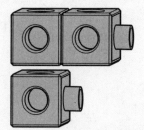

3

odd

even

2.

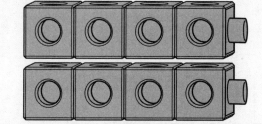

8

odd

even

3.

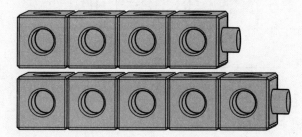

9

odd

even

Reteaching 10-6

Odd and Even Numbers

Draw counters to show each number.
Try to make equal rows. Then circle odd or even.

1. 8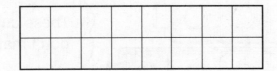

odd

(even)

2. 7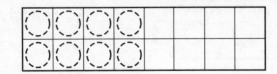

odd

even

3. 15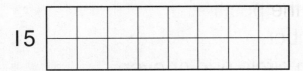

odd

even

4. 16

odd

even

Algebra

5. Find the pattern.

Complete the sentence.

21	22	23	24	25	26	27	28	29	30
31	32	33	34	35	36	37	38	39	40

The shaded numbers are _____.

Ⓐ less than 20   Ⓒ greater than 40

Ⓑ even   Ⓓ odd

Ordinals Through Twentieth

Ordinal numbers tell position.

1st 2nd 3rd 4th 5th 6th 7th 8th 9th 10th

↑This girl is 1st in line. ↑This boy is 6th in line.

Follow the directions to show the position of the flowers.

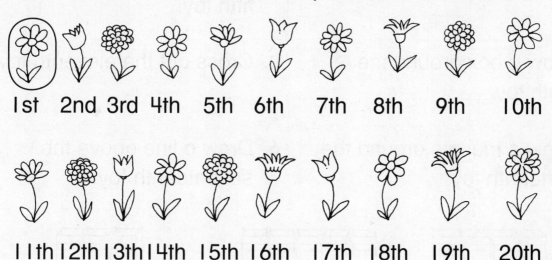

1st 2nd 3rd 4th 5th 6th 7th 8th 9th 10th

11th 12th 13th 14th 15th 16th 17th 18th 19th 20th

1. Circle the 1st flower in blue.

2. Circle the 10th flower in red.

3. Cross out the 18th flower.

4. Circle the 12th flower in yellow.

5. Draw a box around the flower that is 15th.

6. Circle the 5th flower in green.

Ordinals Through Twentieth

1st

1. Circle the second toy.

2. Draw a line under the fifth toy.

3. Draw a box around the ninth toy.

4. Cross out the eleventh toy.

5. Draw a triangle around the thirteenth toy.

6. Draw a line above the seventeenth toy.

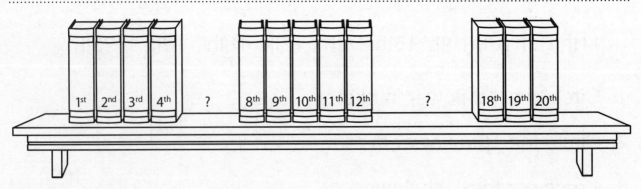

1st 2nd 3rd 4th ? 8th 9th 10th 11th 12th ? 18th 19th 20th

Reasoning

7. How many books are missing?

Ⓐ 10 Ⓑ 9 Ⓒ 8 Ⓑ 7

Patterns in Tables

You can use a table to find how many mittens the children are wearing.

Number of Children	Number of Mittens
1	2
2	4
3	6
4	8

1 child is wearing 2 mittens.

2 children are wearing 4 mittens.

3 children are wearing 6 mittens.

To find the pattern, look at how far apart each number is. The number of mittens increases by 2 each time! If there are 4 children, there will be 8 mittens.

1. If you had 4 bags, how many pens would you have?

Number of Bags	Number of Pens
1	5
2	10
3	15
4	20

2. If there were 4 shelves, how many books would there be?

Number of Shelves	Number of Books
1	5
2	10
3	15

3. If there were 8 sheets, how many stickers would there be?

Number of Sheets	Number of Stickers
1	5
2	10
3	15

Patterns in Tables

Find the pattern. Complete the table.

1.

Number of Ice Cream Cones	Number of Scoops
1	2
2	4
3	6
4	

2.

Number of Boxes	Number of Crackers
1	10
2	20
3	
4	

Algebra

3. Which number completes the table?

Number of Tanks	Number of Fish
1	5
2	10
3	?
4	20

- Ⓐ 11
- Ⓑ 14
- Ⓒ 15
- Ⓓ 25

Problem Solving:
Look for a Pattern

The children need mittens.
Each child has two hands.
How many mittens are needed for all of the children?

You need to find how many hands the children
have altogether.

Make a table to show a pattern.
Write the numbers.

Count the children by 1s.
Count the mittens by 2s.

Number of Children	1	2		
Number of Mittens	2	4		

_8_ mittens will be needed for all of the children.
Does your answer make sense?

Find the pattern. Write the numbers.

1. There are 4 boxes.
   Each box has 5 crayons.
   How many crayons are
   there in all?

Number of Boxes	1	2		
Number of Crayons	5			

   There are _____ crayons in all.

Problem Solving:
Look for a Pattern

Find the pattern.
Write the numbers.

1. There are 6 dragonflies.
   Each dragonfly has 4 wings.
   How many wings are there in all?

Number of Dragonflies	1					
Number of Wings	4					

2. There are 5 tricycles.
   Each tricycle has 3 wheels.
   How many wheels are there in all?

Number of Tricycles					
Number of Wheels					

Reasoning

3. There are 7 boxes.
   Each box has 10 balls in it.
   How many balls are there in all?

(A) 3

(B) 7

(C) 10

(D) 70

Counting with Groups of 10 and Leftovers

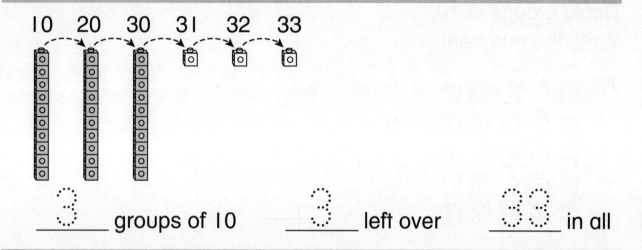

_3_ groups of 10   _3_ left over   _33_ in all

Use counters to show the snap cubes.
Make groups of 10.
Then write the numbers.

1.

_2_ groups of ten

_7_ left over

_____ in all

2.

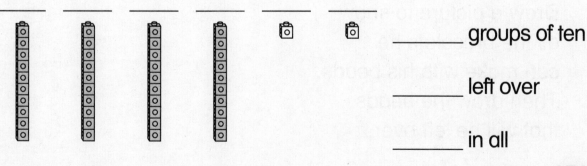

_____ groups of ten

_____ left over

_____ in all

Counting with Groups of 10 and Leftovers

Circle groups of 10.
Write the numbers.

1.

_____ is _____ groups of 10 and _____ left over.

2.

_____ is _____ groups of 10 and _____ left over.

Journal

3. 10 beads fit on a bracelet.
Ben has 34 beads.
Draw a picture to show
all the bracelets he
can make with his beads.
Then draw the beads
that will be left over.

Numbers Made with Tens

You can count the models to find out
how many groups of ten.

1 ten is 10.   2 tens   3 tens   4 tens
is 20.   is 30.   is 40.

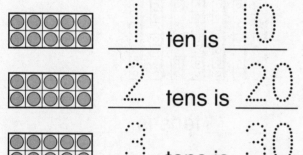

1 ten is 10.

2 tens is 20.

1 ten is 10.

2 tens is 20.

3 tens is 30.

2 tens is _20_.   3 tens is _30_.   4 tens is _40_.

Count the models. Write how many. Then write the number.

1.

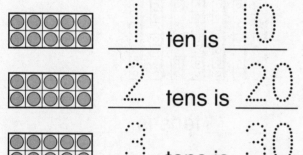

_1_ ten is _10_

_2_ tens is _20_

_3_ tens is _30_

_3_ tens is _30_.

2.

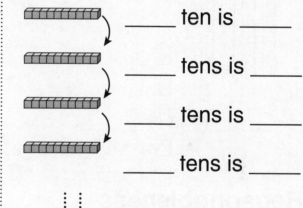

____ ten is ____

____ tens is ____

____ tens is ____

____ tens is ____

_4_ tens is ____.

3.

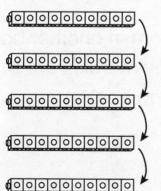

____ ten is ____

____ tens is ____

____ tens is ____

____ tens is ____

____ tens is ____

____ tens is ____.

Numbers Made with Tens

Count by 10s.
Write the numbers.

1.

_____ tens is _____.

2.

_____ tens is _____.

3.

_____ tens is _____.

4.

_____ tens is _____.

Reasonableness

5. What number is shown?

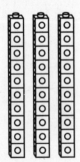

Ⓐ 3
Ⓑ 10
Ⓒ 12
Ⓓ 30

Algebra

6. Nancy has 50 marbles.
30 of the marbles are in
one bag.
The rest are in another bag.
How many marbles are in
the second bag?

Ⓐ 40
Ⓑ 30
Ⓒ 20
Ⓓ 10

Tens and Ones

The chart shows

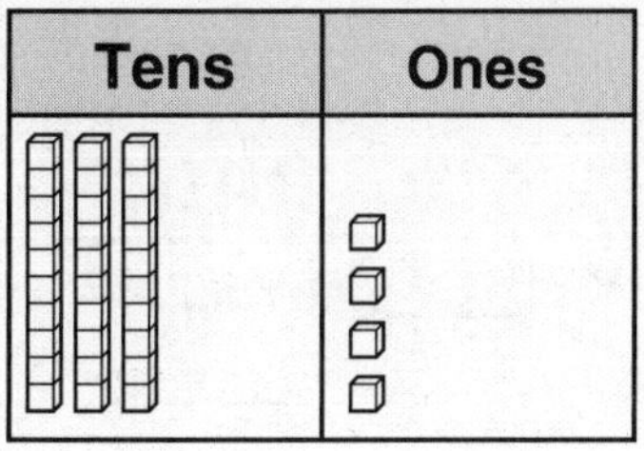

Tens	Ones
▤▤▤	▫▫▫▫

3 tens   4 ones

3 tens is 30
4 ones is 4
30 + 4 = 34

34 is the same as
3 tens and 4 ones.

Count the tens and ones. Then write the numbers.

1.

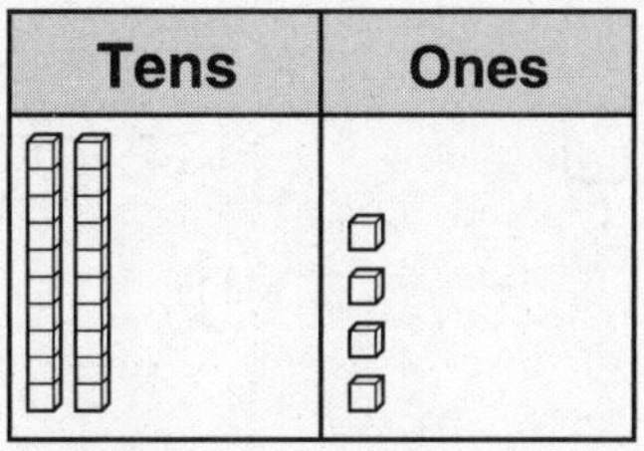

Tens	Ones
▤▤	▫▫▫▫

__2__ tens and __4__ ones

__2__ tens is __20__
__4__ ones is __4__

__20__ + __4__ = __24__

2.

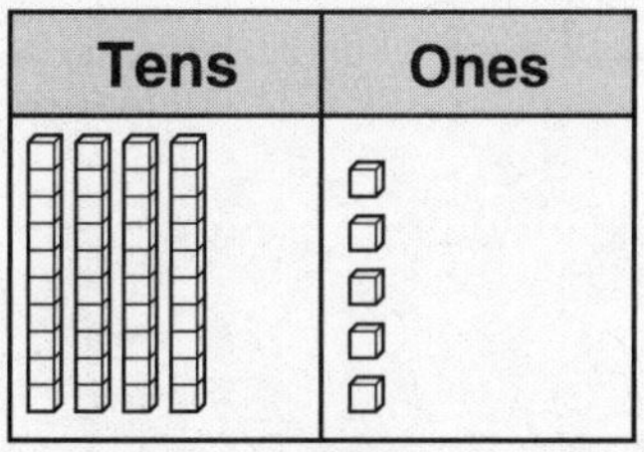

Tens	Ones
▤▤▤▤	▫▫▫▫

_____ tens and _____ ones

_____ tens is _____
_____ ones is _____

_____ + _____ = _____

3.

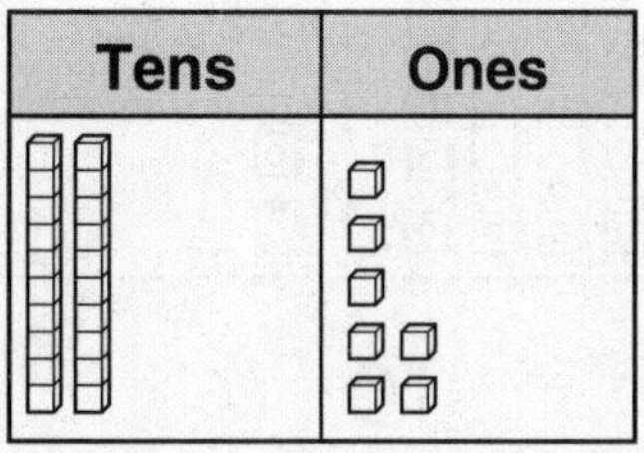

Tens	Ones
▤▤	▫▫▫▫▫▫

_____ tens and _____ ones

_____ tens is _____
_____ ones is _____

_____ + _____ = _____

Reteaching 11-3

Tens and Ones

Count the tens and ones. Then write the numbers.

1.

Tens	Ones

⇒

Tens	Ones
4	5

⇒ 45

2.

Tens	Ones

⇒

Tens	Ones

⇒ _____

3.

Tens	Ones

⇒

Tens	Ones

⇒ _____

Estimation

4. About how many cubes
are shown in the picture?

Tens	Ones

70	50	30	10
Ⓐ	Ⓑ	Ⓒ	Ⓓ

Expanded Form

Two-digit numbers are made up of tens and ones.
27 is a two-digit number.

Tens	Ones

2 is in the tens column.
7 is in the ones column.

tens ones

___2___ tens + ___7___ ones = __27__

1.

tens ones

Tens	Ones

___3___ tens + ___5___ ones = __35__

2.

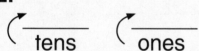
tens ones

Tens	Ones

_____ tens + _____ ones = _____

3.

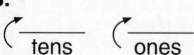
tens ones

Tens	Ones

_____ tens + _____ ones = _____

Expanded Form

Draw the tens and ones. Then write the numbers.

1.

Tens	Ones

___3___ tens + ___6___ ones = ___36___

___30___ + ___6___ = ___36___

2.

Tens	Ones

_____ tens + _____ ones = _____

_____ + _____ = _____

3.

Tens	Ones

_____ tens + _____ ones = _____

_____ + _____ = _____

Reasoning

4. The number in the tens place is even,
and it is greater than 6.
The digit in the ones place is odd,
and it is between 3 and 7.
Which number matches the clues?

(A)   95

(B)   94

(C)   85

(D)   82

Ways to Make Numbers

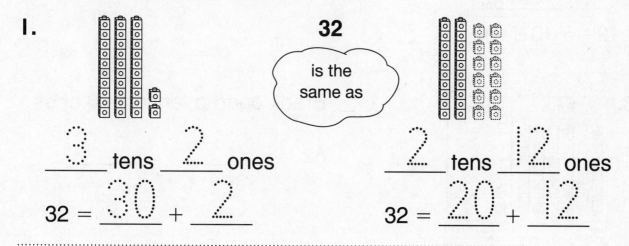

27

is the
same as

27

___2___ tens ___7___ ones

$27 = \underline{20} + \underline{7}$

I ten   17 ones

$27 = \underline{10} + \underline{17}$

Use cubes to show a different way
to make the number. Draw the ones.

1.

32

is the
same as

___3___ tens ___2___ ones

$32 = \underline{30} + \underline{2}$

___2___ tens ___12___ ones

$32 = \underline{20} + \underline{12}$

2.

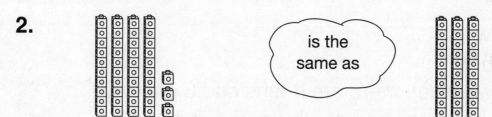

is the
same as

_____ tens _____ ones

$43 = \underline{} + \underline{}$

_____ tens _____ ones

$43 = \underline{} + \underline{}$

Ways to Make Numbers

Use cubes. Show a different way to make the number.

1.

Tens	Ones

37 = 30 + 7

Break apart a ten into 10 ones.

37 = ___20___ + ___17___

2.

Tens	Ones

24 = 10 + 14

Make a ten with 10 ones.

24 = _____ + _____

3.

Tens	Ones

62 = 60 + 2

Break apart a ten into 10 ones.

62 = _____ + _____

Number Sense

4. On Mario's workmat, there are 4 tens and 8 ones.
Which is another way to show this same number?

Ⓐ 6 tens and 6 ones Ⓒ 3 tens and 18 ones

Ⓑ 3 tens and 9 ones Ⓓ 1 ten and 28 ones

Problem Solving:
Make an Organized List

How many ways can you
show 18 with tens and ones?

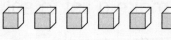
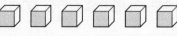

How many tens are in 18? __1__

How many ones are left over? __8__

Tens	Ones
1	8
0	18

Break apart a ten into 10 ones.

How many ones are there? __18__

Make a list to show the ways.

---

1. Olivia wants to show 25
with tens and ones.
Make a list to show the ways.

Tens	Ones
2	5

Reasonableness

2. Penny says there are 4 ways to make 26.
Is she correct?

Yes   No

Problem Solving:
Make an Organized List

Use cubes and make a list to solve.

1. Kelly shows all the ways to make 49 as tens and ones. What ways does she show?

Tens	Ones

2. Marc wants to show 34 as tens and ones. What are all the ways he can show?

Tens	Ones

Reasoning

3. Hector's list shows ways to make 52, but he forgot one way. Which numbers are missing from his list?

Tens	Ones
5	2
?	?
3	22
2	32
1	42
0	52

    Ⓐ   5 and 12

    Ⓑ   4 and 12

    Ⓒ   4 and 22

    Ⓓ   3 and 12

I More, I Less;
10 More, 10 Less

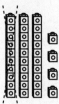

34 take away 10 is 24.

10 less than 34 is __24__.

34 and 10 more is 44.

10 more than 34 is __44__.

Use cubes. Write the numbers.

1.

23 take away I is __22__.

I less than 23 is _____.

23 and I more is __24__.

I more than 23 is _____.

2.

I less than 45 is _____.

I more than 45 is _____.

3.

10 less than 68 is _____.

10 more than 68 is _____.

Reteaching **12-1**

1 More, 1 Less;
10 More, 10 Less

Use cubes. Write the numbers.

1. | 72 |

1 more than _72_ is _73_.

1 less than ____ is ____.

10 more than ____ is ____.

10 less than ____ is ____.

2. | 26 |

1 more than ____ is ____.

1 less than ____ is ____.

10 more than ____ is ____.

10 less than ____ is ____.

3. | 70 |

1 more than ____ is ____.

1 less than ____ is ____.

10 more than ____ is ____.

10 less than ____ is ____.

4. | 14 |

1 more than ____ is ____.

1 less than ____ is ____.

10 more than ____ is ____.

10 less than ____ is ____.

Reasoning

5. Tom is thinking of a number. His number is 10 more than 45. Which number is he thinking of?

(A) 35
(B) 44
(C) 46
(D) 55

6. Shay is thinking of a number. Her number is 1 less than 87. Which number is she thinking of?

(A) 97
(B) 88
(C) 86
(D) 77

Making Numbers
on a Hundred Chart

1	2	3
11	12→	⑬
21	22	23

Go right to find 1 more.
1 more than 12 is 13.

1	2	3
⑪←	12	13
21	22	23

Go left to find 1 less.
1 less than 12 is 11.

1	2	3
11	12	13
21	㉒	23

Go down to find 10 more.
10 more than 12 is 22.

1	②	3
11	12	13
21	22	23

Go up to find 10 less.
10 less than 12 is 2.

Write the missing numbers.

21	22	23	24	25	26	27	28	29	30
31	32	33	34	35	36	37	38	39	40

1. 1 more than 38 is __39__.

2. 1 less than 27 is _____.

3. 10 more than 23 is _____.

4. 10 less than 35 is _____.

Making Numbers
on a Hundred Chart

Use the hundred chart to help.

1	2	3	4	5	6	7	8	9	10
11	12	13	14	15	16	17	18	19	20
21	22	23	24	25	26	27	28	29	30
31	32	33	34	35	36	37	38	39	40
41	42	43	44	45	46	47	48	49	50
51	52	53	54	55	56	57	58	59	60
61	62	63	64	65	66	67	68	69	70
71	72	73	74	75	76	77	78	79	80
81	82	83	84	85	86	87	88	89	90
91	92	93	94	95	96	97	98	99	100

1.

1 more than 77 is _____.

1 less than 77 is _____.

10 more than 77 is _____.

10 less than 77 is _____.

2.

1 more than 82 is _____.

1 less than 82 is _____.

10 more than 82 is _____.

10 less than 82 is _____.

3.

1 more than 73 is _____.

1 less than 73 is _____.

10 more than 73 is _____.

10 less than 73 is _____.

4.

1 more than 90 is _____.

1 less than 90 is _____.

10 more than 90 is _____.

10 less than 90 is _____.

Reasoning

5. Sara has 10 more freckles than Tim.
Tim has 1 less freckle than Hank.
Hank has 65 freckles.
How many freckles does Sara have?

76	74	66	55
Ⓐ	Ⓑ	Ⓒ	Ⓓ

Comparing Numbers
with >, <, =

Write >, <, or =.

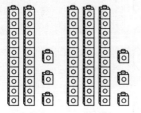 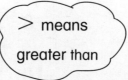 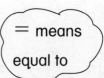

23 < 33   33 > 23   23 = 23

< means
less than

> means
greater than

= means
equal to

23 is **less than** 33   33 is **greater than** 23   23 is **equal to** 23

Circle **less than**, **greater than**, or **equal to.**
Write <, >, or =.

1.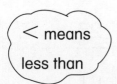

(less than)   greater than   equal to

17 24

2.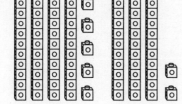

less than   greater than   equal to

45 ◯ 32

3.

less than   greater than   equal to

29 ◯ 29

Comparing Numbers with >, <, =

Write >, <, or =.

1. 43 ⊘ 52

2. 17 ◯ 16

3. 48 ◯ 58

4. 29 ◯ 86

5. 31 ◯ 31

6. 92 ◯ 57

7. 65 ◯ 37

8. 27 ◯ 27

9. 45 ◯ 50

10. 59 ◯ 41

11. 35 ◯ 53

12. 21 ◯ 12

Number Sense

13. Which sentence is true?

38 < 30　　　38 > 30　　　38 = 30　　　30 > 38
Ⓐ　　　　　Ⓑ　　　　　Ⓒ　　　　　Ⓓ

Reasoning

14. Which is equal to 13?

Ⓐ

Ⓑ

Ⓒ

Ⓓ

© Pearson Education, Inc. 1

Ordering Numbers with a Hundred Chart

Use the hundred chart.
Count on from 24.

> Start at 24.
> Count on by 1s.

24, _25_, _26_, _27_

1	2	3	4	5	6	7	8	9	10
11	12	13	14	15	16	17	18	19	20
21	22	23	(24)	25	26	27	28	29	30
31	32	33	34	35	36	37	38	39	40
41	42	43	44	45	46	47	48	49	50
51	52	53	(54)	55	56	57	58	59	60
61	62	63	64	65	66	67	68	69	70
71	72	73	74	75	76	77	78	79	80
81	82	83	84	85	86	87	88	89	90
91	92	93	94	95	96	97	98	99	100

Count back from 54.

> Start at 54.
> Count back by 1s.

54, _53_, _52_, _51_

Write the missing numbers. Look for patterns.

1.

41	42			46	47		
51	52		54	55		58	59	
		63			66	67			70
			74	75		78	

Use the hundred chart to count back by 1s.

2. 29, _28_, _27_, 26 _____, _____, 23

3. 31, _30_, _____, _____, 27, _____, _____

Ordering Numbers with a Hundred Chart

Write the missing numbers.

1.

45	46	47	48
55			
		67	
	76		

2.

61			
		73	74
	82		
91			94

3.

12		14	
	23		
	33		
		44	

4.

	37		
		48	
56			
		68	

Journal

5. Look at the hundred chart.
One number is wrong.
Cross out that number and write
the right number instead.
Then explain how you know.

17	18	19
26	28	29
37	38	39

Number Line Estimation

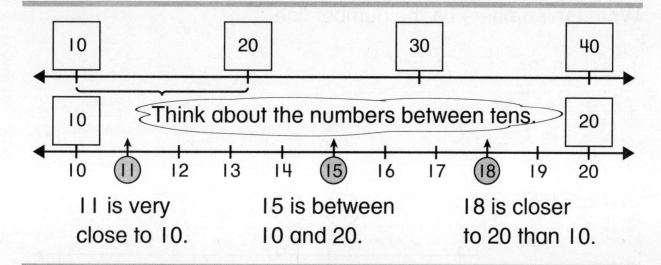

10   20   30   40

10   Think about the numbers between tens.   20

10   11   12   13   14   15   16   17   18   19   20

11 is very
close to 10.

15 is between
10 and 20.

18 is closer
to 20 than 10.

Count by tens to complete the number line.
Then draw lines to show where the numbers go.

1.

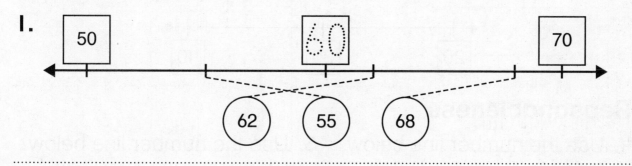

50   60   70

62   55   68

2.

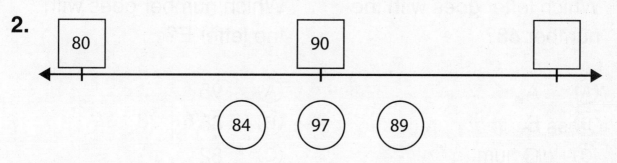

80   90

84   97   89

3.

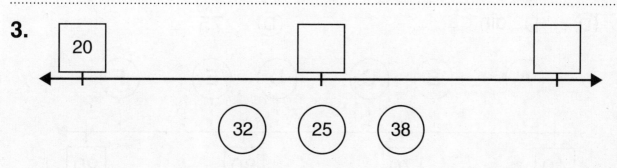

20

32   25   38

Number Line Estimation

Write the numbers on the number line.

1. 31, 48, 36

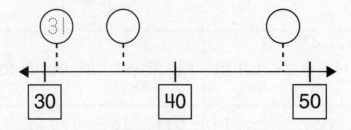

2. 72, 63, 59

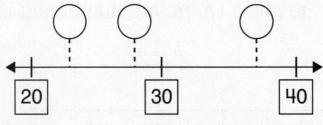

3. 28, 23, 37

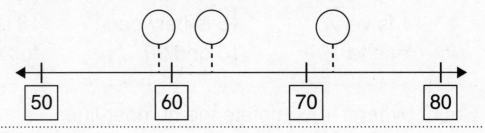

Reasonableness

4. Use the number line below.
Which letter goes with the
number 68?

    Ⓐ A
    Ⓑ B
    Ⓒ C
    Ⓓ D

5. Use the number line below.
Which number goes with
the letter E?

    Ⓐ 95
    Ⓑ 85
    Ⓒ 82
    Ⓓ 75

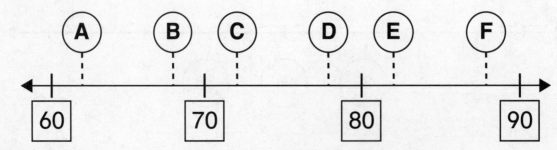

Before, After, and Between

First find 34 on the chart.

1	2	3	4	5	6	7	8	9	10
11	12	13	14	15	16	17	18	19	20
21	22	23	24	25	26	27	28	29	30
31	32	33	(34)	35	36	37	38	39	40
41	42	43	44	45	46	47	48	49	50

Look to the left of 34 to find the number that comes before it.

33 _____ comes **before** 34.

Look to the right of 34 to find the number that comes after it.

35 _____ comes **after** 34.

34 _____ comes **between** 33 and 35.

Write the number that comes before.

1. __23__ , 24   _____ , 47   _____ , 19

Write the number that comes after.

2. 32, __33__   41, _____   27, _____

Write the number that comes between.

3. 22, _____ , 24   45, _____ , 47   32, _____ , 34

Reasoning

Write the number that answers the riddle.

4. I am a number between 10 and 20.
   You say my name when you count by 5s.

   What number am I? _____

Before, After, and Between

Write the number that is one before.

1. _____, 27   _____, 51   _____, 62

2. _____, 76   _____, 45   _____, 34

Write the number that is one after.

3. 41, _____   30, _____   59, _____

4. 85, _____   28, _____   63, _____

Write the number that is between.

5. 21, _____, 23   59, _____, 61   87, _____, 89

6. 45, _____, 47   74, _____, 76   93, _____, 95

Number Sense

7. The number on Fido's dog tag is 1 after 49.

What is the number on Fido's dog tag?

Ⓐ   40

Ⓑ   48

Ⓒ   49

Ⓓ   50

Ordering Three Numbers

The number line can help you put numbers in order.

Show (27) (14) (38) from **least** to **greatest**.

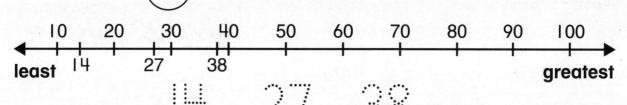

least 14   27   38   greatest

14   27   38
least   greatest

1.

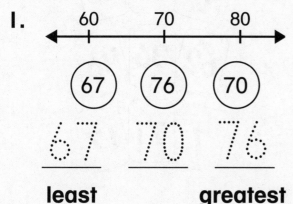

60   70   80

(67) (76) (70)

67   70   76

least   greatest

2.

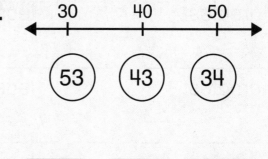

30   40   50

(53) (43) (34)

___ ___ ___

least   greatest

Write the numbers in order from **greatest** to **least**.
Use the number line to help you.

3.

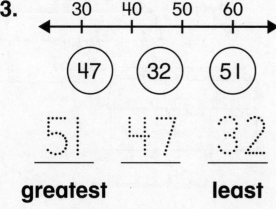

30 40 50 60

(47) (32) (51)

51   47   32

greatest   least

4.

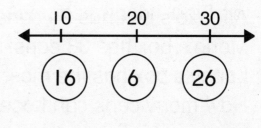

10   20   30

(16) (6) (26)

___ ___ ___

greatest   least

Ordering Three Numbers

Write the numbers in order from
greatest to least.

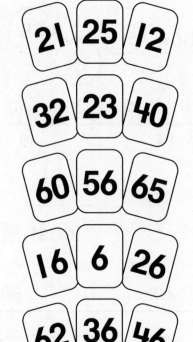

1. <u>25</u> <u>21</u> <u>12</u>
   greatest   least

2. _____ _____ _____
   greatest   least

3. _____ _____ _____
   greatest   least

4. _____ _____ _____
   greatest   least

5. _____ _____ _____
   greatest   least

6. _____ _____ _____
   greatest   least

21	25	12
32	23	40
60	56	65
16	6	26
62	36	46
7	71	17

Number Sense

Order the numbers to solve.

7. Alfonzo's box has 24 cans.
   Maria's box has 33 cans.
   Lacey's box has the most cans.
   How many cans can Lacey's
   box have?

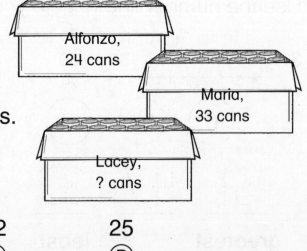

Alfonzo,
24 cans

Maria,
33 cans

Lacey,
? cans

42   33   32   25
Ⓐ   Ⓑ   Ⓒ   Ⓓ

Problem Solving:
Make an Organized List

Kyla picks a number card.
Her number is less than 40.
It is greater than 35.
Which number does she pick?

Make a list to find Kyla's number.

Look at the first clue.
List the numbers in the box
that are less than 40.

29
32
38

Kyla's number could be 29, 32, or 38.

Look at the second clue.
Circle the numbers on the list
that are greater than 35.
38 is greater than 35.

29
32
(38)

Kyla's number must be 38.

I. Ian picks a number card.
His number is even.
It is less than 60.
What number does Ian pick?

Make a list of the even number cards.
Then circle the number on the list
that is less than 60.

_____

_____

_____

Ian's number must be _____.

Problem Solving:
Make an Organized List

Make a list. Write the color of the motorcycle.

| red | pink | orange | yellow | green | blue | purple | black |

1st   8th

1. This motorcycle is between the 3rd motorcycle and the 6th motorcycle.

Which color could it be?

yellow
_____

_____

This motorcycle is the color of the sun. What color is the motorcycle?

_____

2. This motorcycle is between the 1st motorcycle and the 4th motorcycle.

Which color could it be?

_____

_____

This motorcycle is the color of a pumpkin. What color is the motorcycle?

_____

Reasoning

Make a list to find the secret number.

3. I am a number greater than 55.
I am in a square.
What number am I?

Ⓐ   28   Ⓒ   60

Ⓑ   63   Ⓓ   78

 35
 23
 28

 52
 43
 48

 60
 63
 78

Values of Penny and Nickel

A nickel = 5 cents.
Skip count by 5s for nickels.

A penny = 1 cent.
Count by 1s for pennies.

Skip count by 5s for the nickels.
Then count on by 1s for the pennies.

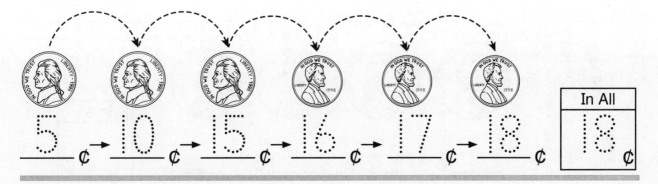

Skip count by 5s and count on by 1s to find
how much money in all.

1.

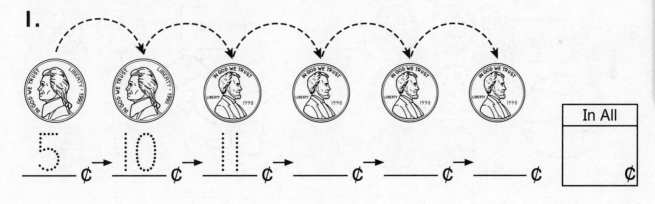

2.

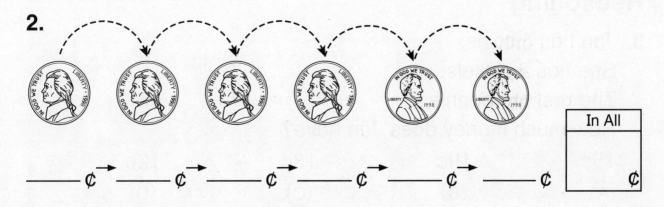

Values of Penny and Nickel

1. Count on. Then write how much money in all.

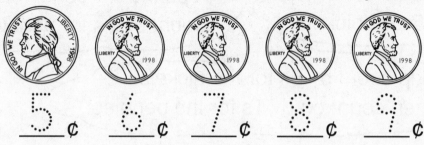

__5__¢   __6__¢   __7__¢   __8__¢   __9__¢

In All
9 ¢

2.

____¢   ____¢   ____¢   ____¢   ____¢

In All
¢

Circle the coins that match each price.

3. 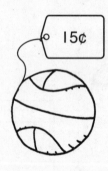 15¢

4. 13¢

Reasoning

5. Jan has 6 coins.

She has 2 nickels.

The rest are pennies.

How much money does Jan have?

15¢   14¢   13¢   12¢

Ⓐ   Ⓑ   Ⓒ   Ⓓ

Values of Penny, Nickel, and Dime

A dime = 10 cents.
Skip count by 10s for dimes.

A penny = 1 cent.
Count by 1s for pennies.

Skip count by 10s. Then count on by 1s.

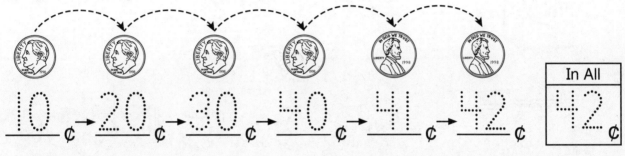

10¢ → 20¢ → 30¢ → 40¢ → 41¢ → 42¢   In All 42¢

Skip count by 10s and count on by 1s
to find how much money in all.

1.

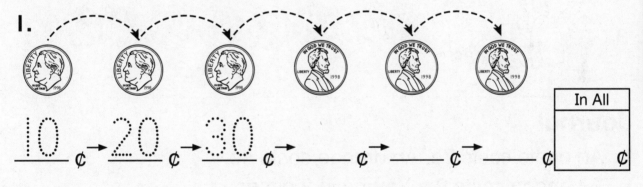

10¢ → 20¢ → 30¢ → ___¢ → ___¢ → ___¢   In All ___¢

2.

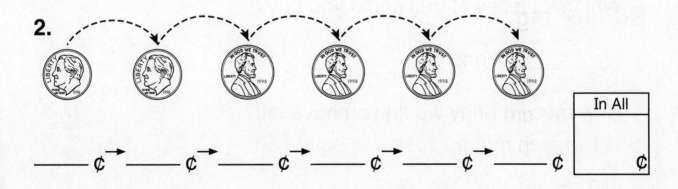

___¢ → ___¢ → ___¢ → ___¢ → ___¢ → ___¢   In All ___¢

Values of Penny, Nickel, and Dime

Circle the coins you could use to buy each item.

1.  25¢

2. 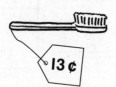 13¢

3.  28¢

Journal

4. An apple costs 7¢. An orange costs 8¢.
A banana costs 9¢. You have 2 dimes.
Which 2 pieces of fruit could you buy?

_____ and _____

How much money would you have left?

_____¢

Value of Quarter

There are different ways you can make 25¢.

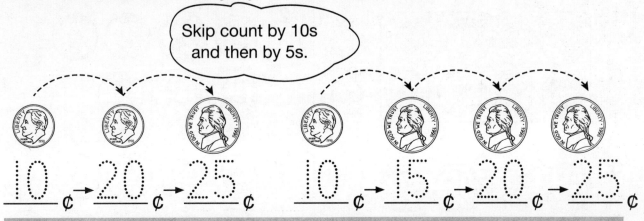

Skip count by 10s
and then by 5s.

Count each group of coins.

Circle the group of coins in each row that equals 25¢.

1.

2.

3.

Visual Thinking

4. Chris has 4 coins in her purse.
They are worth 25¢ in all.
Draw the other 2 coins.

Value of Quarter

Circle the coins that equal 25¢.

1.

2.

3.

4.

5.

Number Sense

6. Kate has 25¢ in her purse.
Which coins does she have?

Ⓐ

Ⓑ

Ⓒ

Ⓓ

Values of Half Dollar and Dollar

Here are some ways to show one dollar.

dollar bill

$1.00 = 100¢

dollar coin

 or

$1.00 = 100¢

4 quarters

2 half-dollar coins

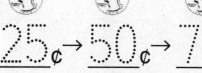

half-dollar = 50¢

2 half-dollars = 100¢

4 quarters = 100¢

Circle the group of coins in each row that makes $1.00.

1.

2.

3.

Values of Half Dollar and Dollar

Circle the coins that equal $1.00.

1.

2.

3.

Reasoning

4. Which shows the same amount?

 Ⓐ

 Ⓑ

 Ⓒ

 Ⓓ

Counting Sets of Coins

 >  > > >

Count the coins.
Start with the coin that is worth the most money.

Remember > stands for greater than.

In All
91 ¢

$\underline{50}_¢$ $\underline{75}_¢$ $\underline{85}_¢$ $\underline{90}_¢$ $\underline{91}_¢$

Skip count. Then write how much money in all.

1.

_____ ¢ _____ ¢ _____ ¢ _____ ¢ _____ ¢

In All
¢

2.

_ ¢ _ ¢ _____ ¢ _ ¢ _ ¢

In All
¢

Counting Sets of Coins

Skip count. Then write how much money in all.

1.

_____¢   _____¢   _____¢   _____¢   _____¢

In All
¢

2.

_____¢   _____¢   _____¢

In All
¢

Journal

3. You have 50¢ in all.
   What can you buy for lunch?
   Be sure to include fruit.
   How much will it cost?
   How much will you have left?

   _____

   _____

Menu

Soup............19¢
Ham Sandwich...25¢
Apple............15¢
Grapes........9¢
Bagel............19¢
Muffin...........11¢

Problem Solving:
Try, Check, and Revise

Jim bought 2 toys at the toy fair. Together they cost 11¢.
Which toys did he buy?

  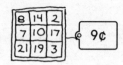 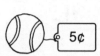

Pick 2 toys. Find their total.

Try  and 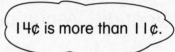 .

Add. ___6___ ¢ + ___8___ ¢ = ___14___ ¢

14¢ is more than 11¢.

Find a toy that costs less than .

The costs less.

Try the  and .

Add. ___6___ ¢ + ___5___ ¢ = ___11___ ¢

Jim bought the  and .

1. Circle the 2 toys that cost 15¢.
Write an addition sentence to
check your answer.

  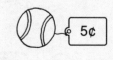

_____¢ + _____¢ = _____¢

Problem Solving:
Try, Check, and Revise

Circle the stickers each child bought.
Write an addition sentence to check.

4¢   5¢   8¢   9¢

1. Venus bought 2 different stickers.
Together they cost 14¢.
What did Venus buy?

_5_ ¢ + _____ ¢ = _____ ¢

2. Kevin bought 2 different stickers.
Together they cost 17¢.
What did Kevin buy?

_____ ¢ + _____ ¢ = _____ ¢

Number Sense

3. Carlos bought 2 different stickers.
Together they cost 9¢.
What did Carlos buy?

Ⓐ    Ⓒ

Ⓑ    Ⓓ

Comparing and Ordering by Length

You can compare and order objects by how long they are.

Line up the objects.

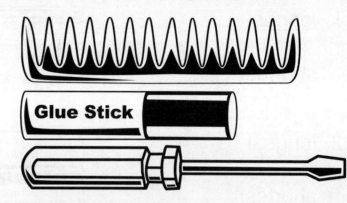

Look to see which object is longest and which is shortest.

Then put the objects in order from longest to shortest.

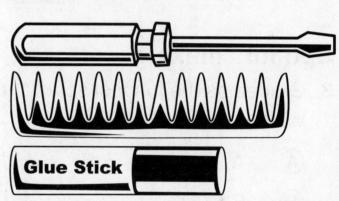

I. Complete the sentences.

Line A _____

Line B _____

Line C _____

Line _____ is the longest.　　Line _____ is the shortest.

Reasoning

2. Use the clues to color the scarves.
The shortest scarf is red.
The green scarf is longer
than the blue scarf.

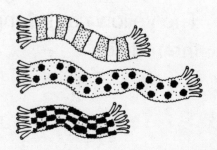

Comparing and Ordering by Length

Draw lines to match the object with the word that describes it.

1. longest

shortest

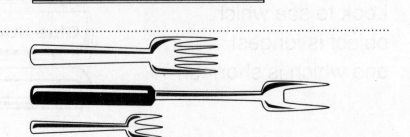

2. longest

shortest

Spatial Thinking

3. Grace has the longest scarf. Which child is Grace?

Ⓐ A

Ⓑ B

Ⓒ C

Ⓓ D

A   B   C   D

Reasoning

4. Use the clues to color the cars.

The shortest car is green.
The yellow car is longer than the red car.

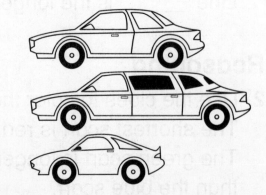

Using Units to Estimate and Measure Length

Look at the paper clip.

Look at the string. ⌒‿‿‿‿‿‿‿‿‿‿‿

Estimate: How many paper clips long is the string?

About ___5___ paper clips long.
Now measure.

> Line up the first paper clip with the edge.

> Be sure paper clips are all the same size.

> Be sure you put the paper clips right next to each other.

Measure: About ___3___ paper clips long.
That is close to the estimate.

Estimate. Then measure using paper clips.

		Estimate	Measure
1.		about _____ ▭	_____ ▭
2.		about _____ ▭	_____ ▭
3.		about _____ ▭	_____ ▭

Using Units to Estimate and Measure Length

Estimate the length. Then use cubes to measure.

	Estimate	Measure

1.

about _____

about _____

2.

Crayon

about _____

about _____

Reasoning

3. Which is the best estimate for the length of the stapler?

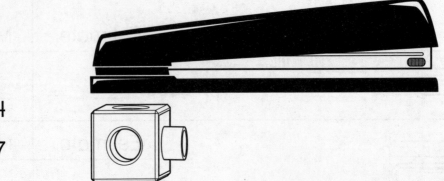

Ⓐ 5

Ⓑ 7

Ⓒ 14

Ⓓ 17

Practice 14-2

Problem Solving:
Use Reasoning

Predict: Will you need more chalk or
more paper clips to measure the marker?

more [   ]   or more ⬭

You must find out if you need more chalk or more paper clips.

Use reasoning to help you.
The paper clip is shorter.
You will probably need more paper clips.

more [   ]   more ⬭

Measure to check your prediction.
Was your prediction correct?

Measure to check.

about __5__ ⬭

about __4__ [   ]

I. Will it take fewer pieces of chalk or fewer paper clips to
measure the stapler? Circle your prediction. Then measure.

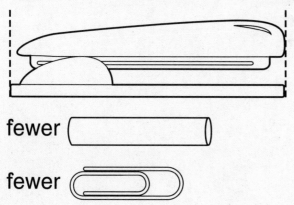

fewer [   ]

fewer ⬭

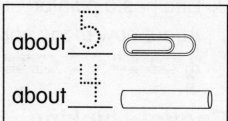

Measure to check.

about _____ ⬭

about _____ [   ]

Problem Solving:
Use Reasoning

Circle your estimate. Measure to check.

Estimate	Measure
1. fewer ☐ fewer ⬭ ✏️ ⊢————————⊣	about _____ ☐ about _____ ⬭
2. more ☐ more ⬭ 🖍 Crayon ⊢————⊣	about _____ ☐ about _____ ⬭

Reasonableness

Circle your answer.

3. Eric has a paintbrush that is about 12 cubes long.
About how many paper clips long could it be?

2 ⬭   7 ⬭   12 ⬭

Spatial Thinking

4. Which object would you need the fewest of
to measure how long the eraser is?

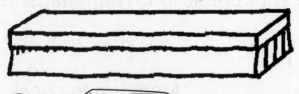

Ⓐ

Ⓑ

Ⓒ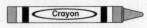

Ⓓ 🖍 Crayon

Feet and Inches

This is 1 inch.

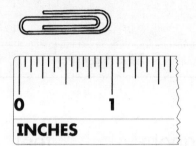

INCHES

Inches are helpful for measuring shorter objects.

It's easier to say "A ribbon is 3 inches long" than "A ribbon is 1/4 of a foot long."

It's also easier to understand.

This is 12 inches.

12 inches is the same as 1 foot.

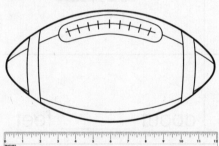

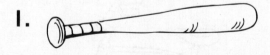

Feet are helpful for measuring longer objects.

It's easier to say "A rug is 6 feet long" than "A rug is 72 inches long."

It's also easier to understand.

Look at the items below. Decide if you would use inches or feet to measure. Circle your answer.

1.    **inches**   **feet**

2.    **inches**   **feet**

3.   **inches**   **feet**

Reteaching 14-4

Feet and Inches

Find each object in your classroom.
Estimate its length.
Then measure using a ruler.

		Estimate	Measure
I.		about _____ feet	about _____ feet
2.		about _____ feet	about _____ feet
3.		about _____ feet	about _____ feet

Reasonableness

4. Which is the best estimate
   for the length of the bicycle?

   Ⓐ   about 4 inches

   Ⓑ   about 9 inches

   Ⓒ   about 4 feet

   Ⓓ   about 9 feet

Centimeters

This is 1 centimeter high.   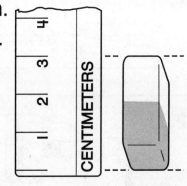 About how many centimeters high is this eraser?

The eraser is about ___2___ centimeters high.
Use a centimeter ruler to measure the eraser.

The eraser measures ___3___ centimeters.
The estimate is close.

Estimate the height. Then measure using a centimeter ruler.

1. 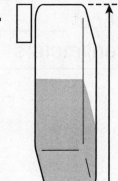 Estimate.

about _____
centimeters

Measure.

about _____
centimeters

2. 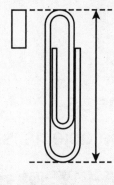 Estimate.

about _____
centimeters

Measure.

about _____
centimeters

3.  Estimate.

about _____
centimeters

Measure.

about _____
centimeters

4. 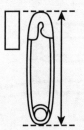 Estimate.

about _____
centimeters

Measure.

about _____
centimeters

Centimeters

Find each object in your classroom.
Estimate the length.
Then measure using a centimeter ruler.

	Estimate	Measure
1. 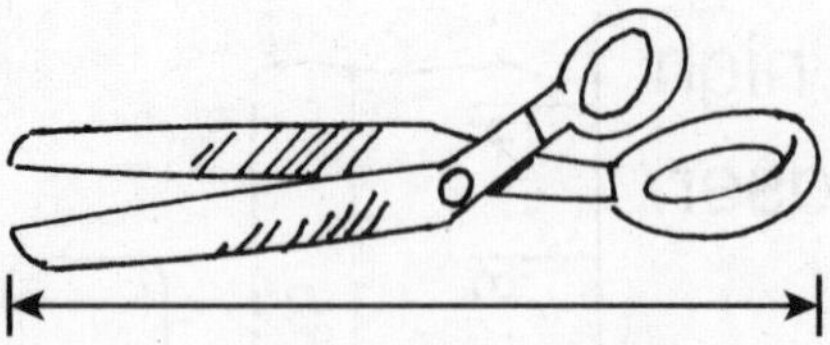	about _____ centimeters	about _____ centimeters
2. 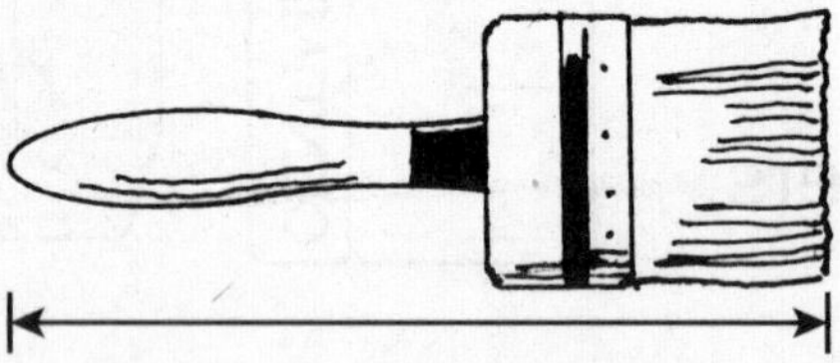	about _____ centimeters	about _____ centimeters
3. 	about _____ centimeters	about _____ centimeters

Reasonableness

4. Which of these objects is longer than 10 centimeters?

Ⓐ

Ⓑ

Ⓒ

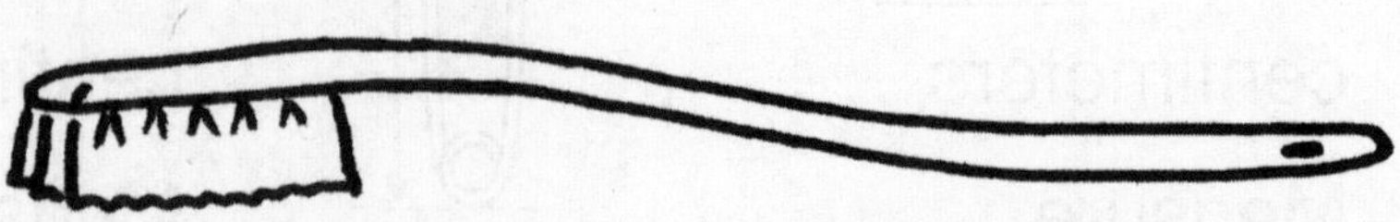

Ⓓ SOAP

Understanding Perimeter

Count the inches around a shape to find the perimeter.

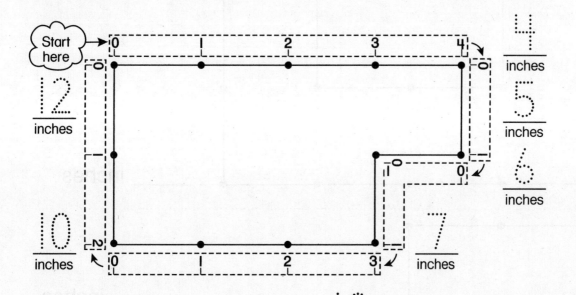

The perimeter of the shape is __12__ inches.

How many inches around each shape?

1.

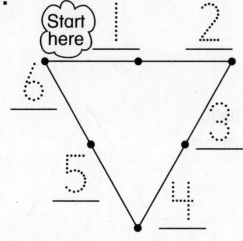

The perimeter
of the triangle is _____ inches.

2.

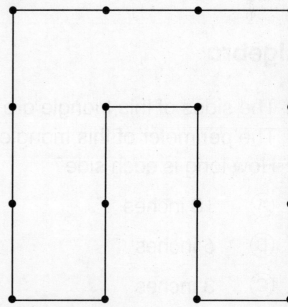

The perimeter
of the shape is _____ inches.

Reteaching 14-6

Understanding Perimeter

Count how many inches around each shape.

1.

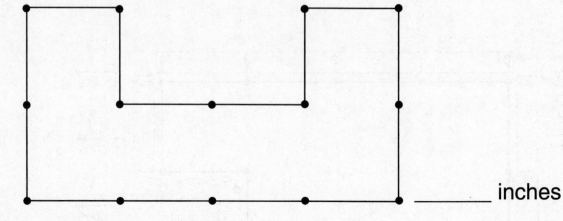

_____ inches

2.

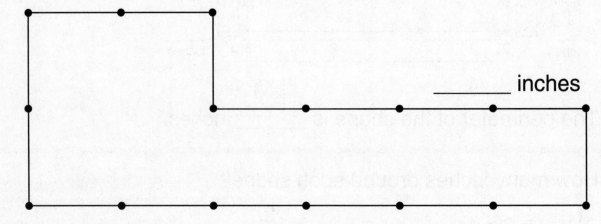

_____ inches

Algebra

3. The sides of this triangle are all equal.
The perimeter of this triangle is 6 inches.
How long is each side?

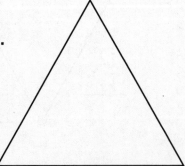

(A)   18 inches

(B)   6 inches

(C)   3 inches

(D)   2 inches

Comparing and Ordering by Capacity

Capacity is the measure of how much a container can hold. A large container will hold more than a small container.

> This pitcher is the largest container. It holds more than the glass and the spoon. It holds the most.

> The spoon is the smallest container. It holds the least.

Use what you notice about size to order by capacity.

1. Draw lines to match the container with the words that describe it.

holds the most

holds the least

Estimation

2. Circle the containers that hold about the same amount.

Comparing and Ordering by Capacity

1. Circle the container you think holds the most.

2. Circle the container you think holds the least.

Reasoning

Use the clues. Put the buckets in order.
Write the color names.

3. The green bucket holds more than the blue bucket.
The red bucket holds less than the blue bucket.

_____   _____   _____

holds the most   holds the least

4. Which sentence describes the pots?

Ⓐ   A holds the least.

Ⓑ   A holds the most.

Ⓒ   B holds the most.

Ⓓ   C holds the most.

Cups, Pints, and Quarts

cup pint quart

Estimate. How much milk will fill the pitcher?

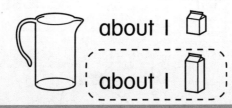

about 1 🥛

about 1 🥛

Circle the better estimate.

1.

about 1 🥛

about 1 🥛

2.

about 1 🥛

about 1 🥛

3.

more than 1 🥛

less than 1 🥛

4.

more than 1 🥛

less than 1 🥛

Cups, Pints, and Quarts

Circle the better estimate.

1.    more than I pint

less than I pint

2.    more than I cup

less than I cup

3.    more than I cup

less than I cup

4.    more than I quart

less than I quart

5.    more than I pint

less than I pint

6.    more than I cup

less than I cup

Reasoning

7. I quart = 2 pints.

2 quarts = _____ pints

  Ⓐ   I

  Ⓑ   2

  Ⓒ   4

  Ⓓ   8

Liters

Estimate how much each real object will hold when filled.

A small container holds a little.

A large container holds a lot.

Less than a liter	About a liter	More than a liter

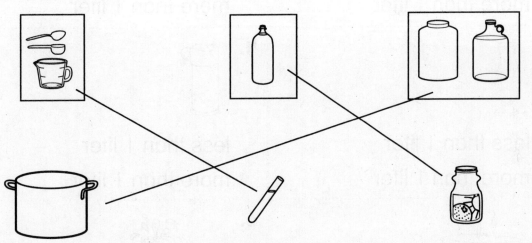

Draw a line to the best estimate.

1.

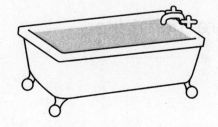

less than 1 liter

more than 1 liter

2.

less than 1 liter

more than 1 liter

3.
Apple Juice

less than 1 liter

more than 1 liter

Liters

Circle the better estimate.

1.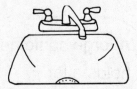

less than 1 liter
more than 1 liter

2.

less than 1 liter
more than 1 liter

3.

less than 1 liter
more than 1 liter

4.

less than 1 liter
more than 1 liter

5.

less than 1 liter
more than 1 liter

6.

less than 1 liter
more than 1 liter

Reasoning

7. About how much water
will you need to fill this fish tank?

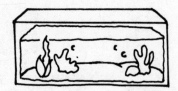

   Ⓐ   about 10 liters

   Ⓑ   about 1 liter

   Ⓒ   about 4 quarts

   Ⓓ   about 1 cup

Comparing and Ordering by Weight

Weight is the measure of how heavy or light an object is.
You can compare objects by weight.

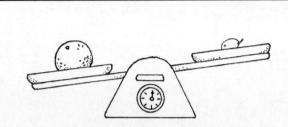

The orange is heavier than the grape.	The pineapple is heavier than the orange.

After you compare the objects, you can order them by weight.

heaviest   lightest

---

1. Draw lines to match the object
with the word that describes it.

heaviest

lightest

Estimation

2. Circle the fruits that weigh about the same amount.

Comparing and Ordering by Weight

Circle the object that is the heaviest.

1.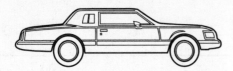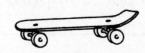

Circle the object that is the lightest.

2.

Spatial Thinking

Use the pictures to answer the questions.

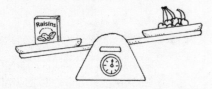 

3. Which object is the heaviest?   **4.** Which object is the lightest?

_____   _____

5. Which list shows the vegetables in order from heaviest to lightest?

   Ⓐ   squash, peas, tomato

   Ⓑ   peas, tomato, squash

   Ⓒ   tomato, squash, peas

   Ⓓ   squash, tomato, peas

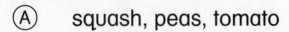

Pounds

This weight is 1 pound.

The light bulb weighs less than 1 pound.

The melon weighs about 1 pound.

The dog weighs more than 1 pound.

Circle the better estimate.

1.

| less than 1 pound | more than 1 pound  |

2.

| less than 1 pound | more than 1 pound |

3.

| less than 1 pound | more than 1 pound |

Pounds

Circle the better estimate.

1.   less than I pound

more than I pound

2.   less than I pound

more than I pound

3.   less than I pound

more than I pound

4.   less than I pound

more than I pound

5.   less than I pound

more than I pound

6.   less than I pound

more than I pound

7.   less than I pound

more than I pound

8.   less than I pound

more than I pound

Algebra

9. Marco needs 8 pounds of apples.
Each bag holds 2 pounds of apples.
How many bags of apples
does Marco need to buy?

2   4   6   10
Ⓐ   Ⓑ   Ⓒ   Ⓓ

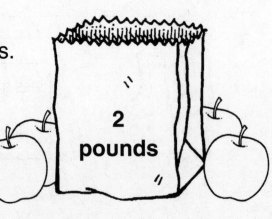

2
pounds

Grams and Kilograms

This feather measures about 1 gram.
1 gram is lighter than 1 kilogram.

This book measures about 1 kilogram.
1 kilogram is heavier than 1 gram

Circle the better estimate.

1.  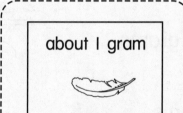 about 1 gram  about 1 kilogram

2.  about 1 gram  about 1 kilogram

3.  about 1 gram 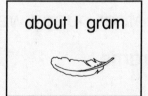 about 1 kilogram

Grams and Kilograms

Circle the better estimate.

1.  grams

kilograms

2.  grams

kilograms

3.  grams

kilograms

4.  grams

kilograms

5.  grams

kilograms

6.  grams

kilograms

7.  grams

kilograms

8.  grams

kilograms

Number Sense

9. Cindy has 2 puppies. They weigh 7 kilograms in all.
One puppy weighs 3 kilograms.
How much does the other puppy weigh?

3 +_____ = 7 kilograms

Ⓐ 3

Ⓑ 4

Ⓒ 5

Ⓒ 10

Comparing and Ordering by Temperature

Temperature tells you how hot or cold something is.
You can compare objects by temperature.

 Ice water is colder than bath water.		Soup is hotter than bath water.

After you compare the objects, you can order them by temperature.

hottest

coldest

I. Draw lines to match the object
with the word that describes it.

hottest

coldest

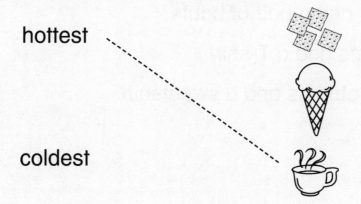

Comparing and Ordering by Temperature

Draw lines to match an object with each word.

1.

hottest   ----coldest

Spatial Thinking

Use the clues to put the mugs in order. Write the color.

2. The red mug is hotter
than the black mug.
The blue mug is cooler
than the black mug.

_____   _____   _____

hottest   coldest

3. What would you wear on the hottest day of the year?

   Ⓐ   jeans and a light jacket

   Ⓑ   a winter coat and a pair of boots

   Ⓒ   a pair of shorts and a T-shirt

   Ⓓ   a pair of sweatpants and a sweatshirt

Understanding the Hour and Minute Hands

The hour hand points to the 6.

hour hand ___6___

The minute hand points to the 12.

minute hand ___12___

When the minute hand points to 12, say o'clock.

___6___ o'clock

Write the time shown on each clock.

1.

hour hand ___3___

minute hand ___12___

___3___ o'clock

2.

hour hand _____

minute hand _____

_____ o'clock

3.

hour hand _____

minute hand _____

_____ o'clock

4.

hour hand _____

minute hand _____

_____ o'clock

Reasoning

Write the times that come next.

5. 4 o'clock   5 o'clock   _____ o'clock

6. 9 o'clock   10 o'clock   _____ o'clock

Understanding the Hour and Minute Hands

Draw an hour hand and a minute hand to show each time.

1.

7 o'clock

2.

10 o'clock

3.

2 o'clock

4.

1 o'clock

5.

8 o'clock

6.

11 o'clock

Algebra

7. Mark the missing time.

2 o'clock, _____, 4 o'clock

Ⓐ 1 o'clock

Ⓑ 3 o'clock

Ⓒ 5 o'clock

Ⓓ 9 o'clock

8. Mark the missing time.

4 o'clock, _____, 6 o'clock

Ⓐ 10 o'clock

Ⓑ 5 o'clock

Ⓒ 3 o'clock

Ⓓ 2 o'clock

Telling and Writing Time to the Hour

Both clocks show 4 o'clock.

 4 tells the hour and...

...00 tells the minutes.

The clocks show the same time.

Draw lines to match the clocks that show the same time.

1.

5:00   **7:00**

2.

1:00   **3:00**

3.

12:00   **9:00**

4.

5:00   **6:00**

Telling and Writing Time to the Hour

Draw the hands on each clock face.
Then write the time on the other clock.

1.

12 o'clock

2.

3 o'clock

3.

7 o'clock

4.

10 o'clock

Reasoning

5. Mark the clock that shows the same time as this clock.

Ⓐ 12:00

Ⓑ 7:00

Ⓒ 8:00

Ⓓ 9:00

Telling and Writing Time to the Half Hour

When it is 7:30, the hour hand will be halfway between __7__ and __8__.
The minute hand will be on __6__.

The hour hand is shorter than the minute hand.

Complete the sentences.
Then draw the hands on the clock face.

I.

The hour hand will be halfway between __3__ and __4__.

The minute hand will be on __6__.

2.

The hour hand will be halfway between _____ and _____.

The minute hand will be on _____.

3.

The hour hand will be halfway between _____ and _____.

The minute hand will be on _____.

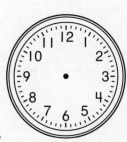

Reteaching 15-3

Telling and Writing Time to the Half Hour

Write the time shown on each clock.

1.

2.

3.

4.

Journal

5. Show 3:00 on the first clock.
On the second clock, show the time
30 minutes later.
Is the hour hand still on 3?
Explain.

_____

_____

_____

Estimating and Ordering Lengths of Time

About how long does each activity take?
You can estimate to find the answer.

(I minute)
I hour
I day

I minute
(I hour)
I day

I minute
I hour
(I day)

About how long does each activity take?
Circle your estimate.

1.

Do homework.

about I minute
(about I hour)
about I day

2.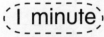

Wash hands.

about I minute
about I hour
about I day

3.

Build a doghouse.

about I minute
about I hour
about I day

4.

Play a game.

about I minute
about I hour
about I day

Estimating and Ordering Lengths of Time

About how long does each activity take?
Mark your estimate.

1.

Ⓐ   about 1 minute

Ⓑ   about 1 hour

Ⓒ   about 1 day

Ⓓ   about 2 days

2.

Ⓐ   about 2 minutes

Ⓑ   about 2 hours

Ⓒ   about 1 day

Ⓓ   about 2 days

Reasoning

3. Jon wakes up in the morning
and gets ready for school.
He gets dressed, brushes his teeth,
and eats breakfast.

Put Jon's activities in order
from the longest to the shortest.

_____   _____   _____
longest   shortest

Using the Calendar

There are 7 days in a week.

(1st day) (2nd day) (3rd day) (4th day) (5th day) (6th day) (7th day)

Sunday, Monday, Tuesday, Wednesday, Thursday, Friday, Saturday

There are 12 months in a year.

January						
Sunday	Monday	Tuesday	Wednesday	Thursday	Friday	Saturday
				1	2	3
4	5	6	7	8	9	10
11	12	13	14	15	16	17
18	19	20	21	22	23	24
25	26	27	28	29	30	31

February						
Sunday	Monday	Tuesday	Wednesday	Thursday	Friday	Saturday
1	2	3	4	5	6	7
8	9	10	11	12	13	14
15	16	17	18	19	20	21
22	23	24	25	26	27	28

March						
Sunday	Monday	Tuesday	Wednesday	Thursday	Friday	Saturday
1	2	3	4	5	6	7
8	9	10	11	12	13	14
15	16	17	18	19	20	21
22	23	24	25	26	27	28
29	30	31				

April						
Sunday	Monday	Tuesday	Wednesday	Thursday	Friday	Saturday
			1	2	3	4
5	6	7	8	9	10	11
12	13	14	15	16	17	18
19	20	21	22	23	24	25
26	27	28	29	30		

May						
Sunday	Monday	Tuesday	Wednesday	Thursday	Friday	Saturday
					1	2
3	4	5	6	7	8	9
10	11	12	13	14	15	16
17	18	19	20	21	22	23
24/31	25	26	27	28	29	30

June						
Sunday	Monday	Tuesday	Wednesday	Thursday	Friday	Saturday
	1	2	3	4	5	6
7	8	9	10	11	12	13
14	15	16	17	18	19	20
21	22	23	24	25	26	27
28	29	30	28	29	30	

July						
Sunday	Monday	Tuesday	Wednesday	Thursday	Friday	Saturday
						1
2	3	4	5	6	7	8
9	10	11	12	13	14	15
16	17	18	19	20	21	22
23/30	24/31	25	26	27	28	29

August						
Sunday	Monday	Tuesday	Wednesday	Thursday	Friday	Saturday
			1	2	3	4	5
6	7	8	9	10	11	12
13	14	15	16	17	18	19
20	21	22	23	24	25	26
27	28	29	30	31		

September						
Sunday	Monday	Tuesday	Wednesday	Thursday	Friday	Saturday
					1	2
3	4	5	6	7	8	9
10	11	12	13	14	15	16
17	18	19	20	21	22	23
24	25	26	27	28	29	30

October						
Sunday	Monday	Tuesday	Wednesday	Thursday	Friday	Saturday
1	2	3	4	5	6	7
8	9	10	11	12	13	14
15	16	17	18	19	20	21
22	23	24	25	26	27	28
29	30	31				

November						
Sunday	Monday	Tuesday	Wednesday	Thursday	Friday	Saturday
			1	2	3	4
5	6	7	8	9	10	11
12	13	14	15	16	17	18
19	20	21	22	23	24	25
26	27	28	29	30		

December						
Sunday	Monday	Tuesday	Wednesday	Thursday	Friday	Saturday
					1	2
3	4	5	6	7	8	9
10	11	12	13	14	15	16
17	18	19	20	21	22	23
24/31	25	26	27	28	29	30

Use the calendar above to answer the questions.

1. Write the names of the missing months.

January, February, _____, April, May,

_____, July, August,_____,

October, November, ~~December~~

2. What day is the last day of January on this calendar?

_____

Using the Calendar

Use this calendar to answer the questions.

	January					
Sunday	Monday	Tuesday	Wednesday	Thursday	Friday	Saturday
				1	2	3
4	5	6	7	8	9	10
11	12	13	14	15	16	17
18	19	20	21	22	23	24
25	26	27	28	29	30	31

	February					
Sunday	Monday	Tuesday	Wednesday	Thursday	Friday	Saturday
1	2	3	4	5	6	7
8	9	10	11	12	13	14
15	16	17	18	19	20	21
22	23	24	25	26	27	28

	March					
Sunday	Monday	Tuesday	Wednesday	Thursday	Friday	Saturday
1	2	3	4	5	6	7
8	9	10	11	12	13	14
15	16	17	18	19	20	21
22	23	24	25	26	27	28
29	30	31				

	April					
Sunday	Monday	Tuesday	Wednesday	Thursday	Friday	Saturday
			1	2	3	4
5	6	7	8	9	10	11
12	13	14	15	16	17	18
19	20	21	22	23	24	25
26	27	28	29	30		

	May					
Sunday	Monday	Tuesday	Wednesday	Thursday	Friday	Saturday
					1	2
3	4	5	6	7	8	9
10	11	12	13	14	15	16
17	18	19	20	21	22	23
24/31	25	26	27	28	29	30

	June					
Sunday	Monday	Tuesday	Wednesday	Thursday	Friday	Saturday
	1	2	3	4	5	6
7	8	9	10	11	12	13
14	15	16	17	18	19	20
21	22	23	24	25	26	27
28	29	30	28	29	30	

	July					
Sunday	Monday	Tuesday	Wednesday	Thursday	Friday	Saturday
						1
2	3	4	5	6	7	8
9	10	11	12	13	14	15
16	17	18	19	20	21	22
23/30	24/31	25	26	27	28	29

	August					
Sunday	Monday	Tuesday	Wednesday	Thursday	Friday	Saturday
	1	2	3	4	5	
6	7	8	9	10	11	12
13	14	15	16	17	18	19
20	21	22	23	24	25	26
27	28	29	30	31		

	September					
Sunday	Monday	Tuesday	Wednesday	Thursday	Friday	Saturday
					1	2
3	4	5	6	7	8	9
10	11	12	13	14	15	16
17	18	19	20	21	22	23
24	25	26	27	28	29	30

	October					
Sunday	Monday	Tuesday	Wednesday	Thursday	Friday	Saturday
1	2	3	4	5	6	7
8	9	10	11	12	13	14
15	16	17	18	19	20	21
22	23	24	25	26	27	28
29	30	31				

	November					
Sunday	Monday	Tuesday	Wednesday	Thursday	Friday	Saturday
		1	2	3	4	
5	6	7	8	9	10	11
12	13	14	15	16	17	18
19	20	21	22	23	24	25
26	27	28	29	30		

	December					
Sunday	Monday	Tuesday	Wednesday	Thursday	Friday	Saturday
					1	2
3	4	5	6	7	8	9
10	11	12	13	14	15	16
17	18	19	20	21	22	23
24/31	25	26	27	28	29	30

1. What day is the first of August?_____

2. What month comes just after May? _____

3. How many months have only 30 days? _____

4. What month comes just before November? _____

Reasoning

5. The last day of May is on a Sunday.
Mike goes to camp on the day after.
Which day does Mike go to camp?

(A) Sunday

(C) Tuesday

(B) Monday

(D) Saturday

Problem Solving:
Use Data from a Table

Nature Center Schedule	
Activity	**Time**
Hike	9:00
Feed Turtles	10:00
Pick Flowers	11:00
Bird Watch	12:00

A schedule tells the time at which activities start.

Look for the activity.

The hike starts at **9:00**.

Look at the time.

At 12:00 we **bird watch**.

Use the schedule to answer the questions. Circle your answer.

I. Which activity comes just before feeding the turtles?

Bird Watch   Hike   Pick Flowers

2. Which activity comes just after picking flowers?

Hike   Feed Turtles   Bird Watch

3. What time does the activity Pick Flowers begin?

9:00   10:00   11:00

4. Which activity starts at 10:00?

Hike   Feed Turtles   Bird Watch

Problem Solving:
Use Data from a Table

Use the schedule to answer the questions.

Time	Activity
9:00	Art
9:30	T-Ball
10:00	Music
10:30	Puppet Theater
11:00	Swimming

1. What activity is at 9:00? _____

2. What activity is just
before Music? _____

3. What activity is just after
Puppet Theater? _____

Reasoning

4. What time does Music begin?

9:00   9:30   10:00   10:30
Ⓐ   Ⓑ   Ⓒ   Ⓓ

Doubles

When you add the same number to itself, you are using doubles.

◇ 1
◇ + 1
‾‾‾‾
   2

◇◇ 2
◇◇ + 2
‾‾‾‾‾
    4

◇◇◇ 3
◇◇◇ + 3
‾‾‾‾‾‾
     6

◇◇◇◇ 4
◇◇◇◇ + 4
‾‾‾‾‾‾‾
      8

Use doubles to add. Draw doubles to help you.

1. ◇◇◇◇◇ 5
        ◇◇◇◇◇ + 5
        ‾‾‾‾‾‾
              10

2. ○○○○○○ 6
                + 6
              ‾‾‾‾‾

3. ○○○○○○○ 7
                 + 7
               ‾‾‾‾‾

4. ○○○○○○○○ 8
                  + 8
                ‾‾‾‾‾

Visual Thinking

5. For each picture write an addition sentence
that tells how many buttons there are.

__3__ + ____ = ____

____ + ____ = ____

Doubles

Add to solve. Then circle the doubles.

1.   5   6   6   8   5   2
   + 5   + 7   + 3   + 8   + 8   + 2
   ____   ____   ____   ____   ____   ____

2.   4   2   7   8   4   5
   + 2   + 7   + 7   + 1   + 4   + 2
   ____   ____   ____   ____   ____   ____

3.   7   5   3   6   9   4
   + 1   + 0   + 3   + 9   + 2   + 4
   ____   ____   ____   ____   ____   ____

4.   6   5   6   9   5   1
   + 6   + 7   + 8   + 9   + 4   + 1
   ____   ____   ____   ____   ____   ____

Reasoning

5. Jack has 5 toy cars. Sam has 5 toy cars.
   Which doubles fact shows how many cars
   they have in all?

   (A) $4 + 4 = 8$
   (B) $5 + 5 = 10$
   (C) $6 + 6 = 12$
   (D) $7 + 7 = 14$

Doubles Plus 1

You can use doubles facts to add 4 + 5.
Because 5 = 4 + 1, you can write 4 + 5 as

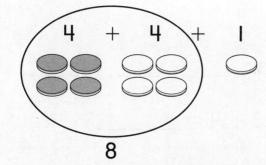

I know 4 + 4 = 8.
I know 8 and 1 more is 9.
So 4 + 5 = 9.

Add to find the doubles and doubles plus 1 facts.

1.

$$3 \atop + \, 3 \over 6$$

$$3 \atop + \, 4 \over 7$$

---

2. Bill has 6 trucks.
Ashley has 7 trucks.
How many trucks do
they have in all?

_____ trucks

3. Peter read 7 books.
Kira read 8 books.
How many books did
they read in all?

_____ books

Doubles Plus 1

Add the doubles.
Then use the doubles to help you add.

1.

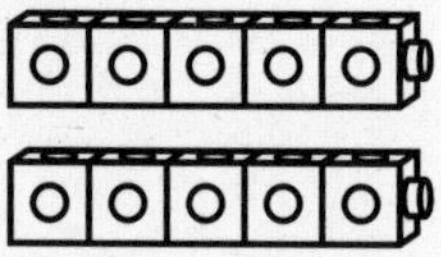

Think __5__ + __5__ = __10__

so 5 + 6 = _____

2.

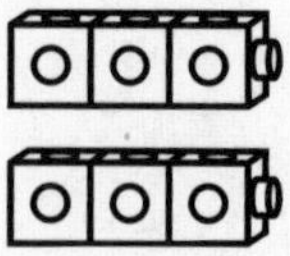

Think ____ + ____ = ____

so 3 + 4 = _____

3.

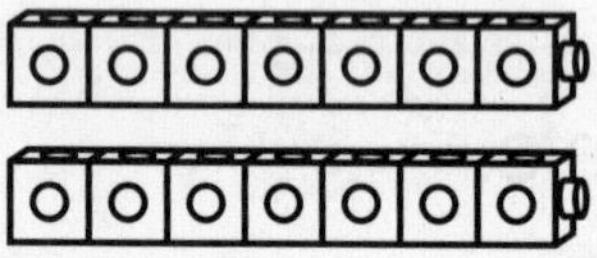

Think ____ + ____ = ____

so 7 + 8 = _____

4.

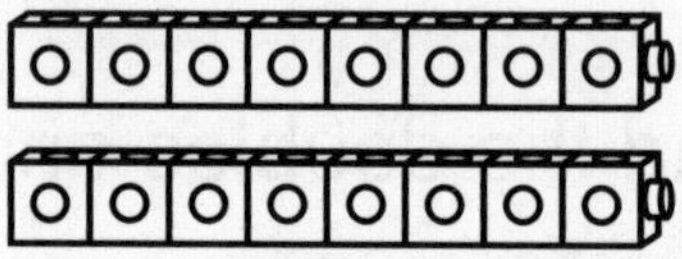

Think ____ + ____ = ____

so 8 + 9 = _____

Number Sense

5. Paco has 5 model cars.
He gets 6 more cars for his birthday.
How many cars does he have now?

Ⓐ 12

Ⓑ 11

Ⓒ 10

Ⓓ 9

Doubles Plus 2

You can use doubles facts to add 6 + 8.
Because 8 = 6 + 2, you can write 6 + 8 as

 6   +    6   +   2

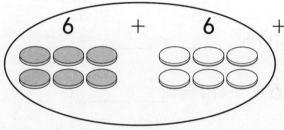

6   +   6   +   2

> I know 6 + 6 = 12.
> I know 12 and 2 more is 14.
> So 6 + 8 = 14.

12

Add to find the doubles and doubles plus 2 facts.

1.   3
   + 3
    6   3
                     + 5
                      8

2.   4 + 6 = _____   **3.**   7 + 9 = _____

4. Max scored 9 runs on Monday
and 11 runs on Tuesday.
How many runs did he score in all?

What doubles fact will you use?

_____ + _____ = _____

so 9 + 11 = _____ runs

Doubles Plus 2

Draw 2 more cubes. Use a doubles fact to help you add.

1. [cubes diagram]

Think _8_ + _8_ = _16_

so 8 + 10 = _____

2. [cubes diagram]

Think ____ + ____ = ____

so 9 + 11 = _____

3. [cubes diagram]

Think ____ + ____ = ____

so 3 + 5 = _____

4. [cubes diagram]

Think ____ + ____ = ____

so 2 + 4 = _____

Journal

5. Write a story about the doubles plus 2 fact 5 + 7 = 12.

_____

_____

_____

_____

Problem Solving:
Two-Question Problems

Jill has 6 marbles. She gets 5 more. $6 + 5 =$ _____ marbles
How many marbles does
she have in all?

I know Jill has 11 marbles in all.
I know she gives Sal 8.
I can subtract to find how many
she has left.

Jill gives 8 marbles to Sal.
Now how many marbles
does Jill have?

$11 - 8 =$ __3__   Jill has __3__ marbles left.

1. Jack has 4 model cars. He gets 3 more model cars.
   How many model cars does Jack have in all?

   __3__ + __4__ = __7__ model cars

   For his birthday Jack gets 5 model cars.
   How many model cars does he have now?

   _____ + _____ = _____ model cars

2. Nicky has 6 charms on her bracelet. She buys 8 more.
   How many charms does Nicky have in all?

   _____ + _____ = _____ charms

   On the way home 4 charms are lost.
   How many charms does Nicky have now?

   _____ − _____ = _____ charms

Problem Solving:
Two-Question Problems

Write number sentences to solve both parts.

1. Peter read 7 books about dinosaurs.
   He read 8 books about sharks.
   How many books did Peter read in all?

   _____ ◯ _____ = _____ books

   Peter did not like 6 of the books he read.
   How many books did Peter like?

   _____ ◯ _____ = _____ books

Journal

Write a second problem to go with the first problem.
Solve your problem.

2. Nate counts dogs at the dog park.
   He sees 9 small dogs and 7 big dogs.
   How many dogs does he see in all?

   $9 + 7 = 16$

   _____

   _____

   _____

Making 10 to Add 9

You can make 10 to find $9 + 7$.
Draw 9 white triangles and 7 gray triangles.
Circle a group of 10. Count the leftover triangles.
Then complete the number sentence.

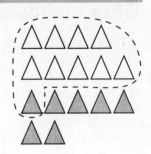

$10 + \underline{6} = 16$, so $9 + 7 = \underline{16}$

Circle a group of 10. Then write 2 addition sentences.

1. Alice picked 9 flowers.
   Tanisha picked 5 flowers.
   How many flowers were
   picked altogether?

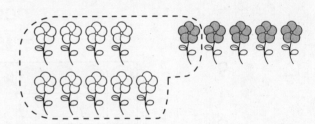

   $10 + \underline{\hspace{2cm}} = 14$, so $9 + 5 = \underline{\hspace{2cm}}$

2. Paul caught 9 ladybugs.
   Cecil caught 3 ladybugs.
   How many ladybugs were
   caught altogether?

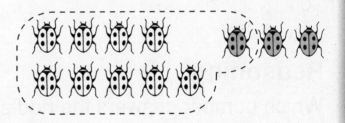

   $10 + \underline{\hspace{2cm}} = \underline{\hspace{2cm}}$, so $9 + 3 = \underline{\hspace{2cm}}$

Algebra

3. Sam has 9 red pens and 8 blue pens. Circle all the
   ways to show how many pens Sam has in all.

   $9 + 8$ $9 + 8 + 7$ $1 + 8 + 8$ $10 + 7$ $10 + 8$

Making 10 to Add 9

Draw counters to help you add. Write the missing addend.
Then write the sums.

1.   9

$+$ 3

     ?

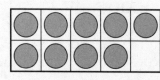

10   9

$+$ [ ]   so $+$ 3

[ ]   [ ]

....

2.   9

$+$ 6

     ?

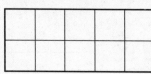

10   9

$+$ [ ]   so $+$ 6

[ ]   [ ]

....

Reasoning

Which number answers the riddle?

3. When you add 9 to me, the sum is
the same as 10 + 8.

(A)   7

(B)   8

(C)   9

(D)   10

Making 10 to Add 8

You can make 10 to find 8 + 6.
Draw 8 white marbles and 6 black marbles.

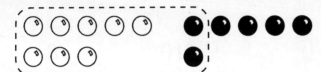

Circle a group of 10. Count the leftover marbles.
Then complete the number sentence.

10 + _____4_____ = 14, so 8 + 6 = _____14_____

Circle a group of 10. Then write 2 addition sentences.

1. Kim has 8 white toy bears.
   Tia has 4 gray toy bears.
   How many bears do they
   have in all?

   10 + _____ = 12, so 8 + 4 = _____

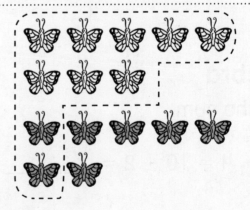

2. Tamika caught 8 butterflies.
   Cecil caught 7 butterflies.
   How many butterflies
   were caught altogether?

   10 + _____ = _____, so 8 + 7 = _____

Making 10 to Add 8

Draw counters to help you add.
Write the missing addend.
Then write the sums.

1.   8
      + 6
      ―――
        ?

       10   8
   [ ]   [ ]
 + [ ]   so   + 6
   ―――   ―――
   [ ]   [ ]

2.   8
      + 3
      ―――
        ?

       10   8
   [ ]   [ ]
 + [ ]   so   + 3
   ―――   ―――
   [ ]   [ ]

Algebra

Find the sum.

3. $8 + 4 = 10 + 2 =$ _____

   11   12   13   14
   Ⓐ   Ⓑ   Ⓒ   Ⓓ

Adding Three Numbers

When you add 3 numbers, look for facts you know.
Then add the other number.

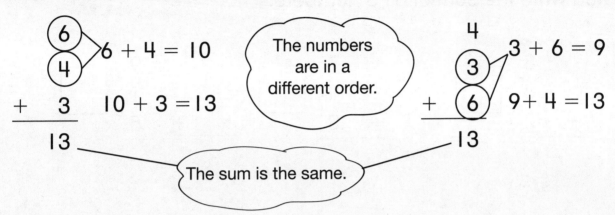

The numbers are in a different order.

The sum is the same.

Find each sum. Add the circled numbers first.
Then add the other number.

1.

⑤
2   5 + 5 = 10
+ ⑤
12   10 + 2 = 12

5
②   2 + 5 = 7
+ ⑤
12   7 + 5 = 12

2.

③
⑥   3 + 6 = ___
+ 4
___ + 4 = ___

3
⑥   6 + 4 = ___
+ ④
___ + 3 = ___

3.

⑦
③   7 + 3 = ___
+ 4
___ + 4 = ___

7
③   3 + 4 = ___
+ ④
___ + 7 = ___

Adding Three Numbers

Circle 2 numbers to add first.
Write their sum in the box.
Then write the sum of all 3 numbers.

1.

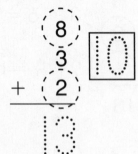

$$
\begin{array}{r}
8 \\
3 \\
+\ 2 \\
\hline
\end{array}
$$

$$
\begin{array}{r}
7 \\
4 \\
+\ 3 \\
\hline
\end{array}
$$

$$
\begin{array}{r}
9 \\
1 \\
+\ 5 \\
\hline
\end{array}
$$

2.

$$
\begin{array}{r}
6 \\
3 \\
+\ 4 \\
\hline
\end{array}
$$

$$
\begin{array}{r}
5 \\
5 \\
+\ 7 \\
\hline
\end{array}
$$

$$
\begin{array}{r}
2 \\
8 \\
+\ 7 \\
\hline
\end{array}
$$

Spatial Thinking

Add the dots on the dominoes.
What is the sum?

3.

Ⓐ 17

Ⓑ 15

Ⓒ 13

Ⓓ 11

Algebra

Find the missing number.

4. $8 + \underline{\quad} + 7 = 17$

Ⓐ 2

Ⓑ 3

Ⓒ 4

Ⓓ 5

Problem Solving: Make a Table

Jan is making groups of flowers.
The flowers are red, blue, and yellow.
Each group has 3 flowers in it.
How many different groups can
Jan make?

To solve the problem,
you need to find how
many different ways
Jan can put the
flowers together.

Red Flowers	Blue Flowers	Yellow Flowers	
3	0	0	You can have 3 flowers of one color.
0	3	0	
0	0	3	
2	1	0	You can have 2 flowers of one color and 1 flower of another color.
2	0	1	
			You can have 1 flower of each color.

Make a table. Then
count how many
ways you made.

1. Complete the table.

2. There are

   _____

   different ways.

3. What is the sum
   of each column
   in your table?

   _____

Problem Solving: Make a Table

Make a table to solve the problem.

1. Jose is making snack packs. He has bags of raisins, nuts, and pretzels. Each snack pack has 3 bags. How many different snack packs can Jose make?

   _____ different
   snack packs

Raisins	Peanuts	Pretzels
3	0	0

2. Max put eggs and bread on a special cooking tray. The tray holds 4 items. If Max puts 2 eggs on the tray, how many pieces of bread can he put on the tray?

   Ⓐ 1

   Ⓑ 2

   Ⓒ 3

   Ⓓ 4

Using Related Facts

These two facts are related.

> The addition sentence and the subtraction sentence have the same 3 numbers.

$9 + 3 = 12$

$12 - 3 = 9$

> The sum of the addition sentence is the first number in the subtraction sentence.

Add. Then write a related subtraction fact.

1.

$8 + 4 = \underline{12}$

$\underline{12} - \underline{4} = \underline{8}$

2.

$7 + 6 = \underline{13}$

$\underline{13} - \underline{6} = \underline{}$

3.

$9 + 2 = \underline{}$

$\underline{} - 9 = \underline{}$

4.

$8 + 5 = \underline{}$

$\underline{} - 8 = \underline{}$

5.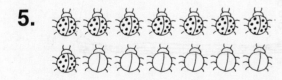

$8 + 6 = \underline{}$

$\underline{} - 8 = \underline{}$

6.

$8 + 7 = \underline{}$

$\underline{} - 8 = \underline{}$

Using Related Facts

Write an addition fact and
a related subtraction fact.

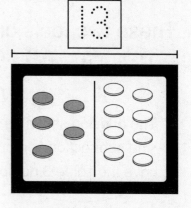

1. ___5___ + ___8___ = ___13___

___13___ - ___8___ = ___5___

2. _____ + _____ = _____

_____ - _____ = _____

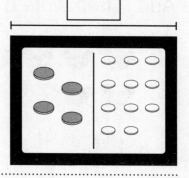

....

Reasoning

Solve the problem.

3. Abby's dad wrote this
addition sentence on
a piece of paper.

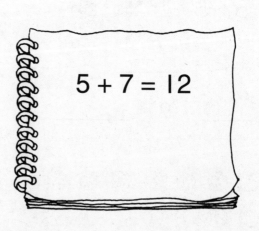

$5 + 7 = 12$

Which subtraction sentence
is related?

  Ⓐ $7 + 5 = 12$

  Ⓑ $12 - 7 = 5$

  Ⓒ $12 - 9 = 3$

  Ⓓ $7 - 5 = 2$

Fact Families

This is a fact family.

$8 + 4 = 12$

$4 + 8 = 12$

$12 - 8 = 4$

$12 - 4 = 8$

Each number sentence has the same 3 numbers.

Complete each fact family. Use counters to help you.

1. | 6 | 11 | 5 |

$6 + 5 = \underline{11}$

$5 + \underline{6} = 11$

$11 - 5 = \underline{6}$

$11 - \underline{6} = 5$

2. | 9 | 5 | 14 |

$9 + 5 = \underline{\hspace{1cm}}$

$5 + \underline{\hspace{1cm}} = 14$

$14 - 5 = \underline{\hspace{1cm}}$

$14 - \underline{\hspace{1cm}} = 5$

3. | 7 | 6 | 13 |

$7 + 6 = \underline{\hspace{1cm}}$

$6 + \underline{\hspace{1cm}} = 13$

$13 - 6 = \underline{\hspace{1cm}}$

$13 - \underline{\hspace{1cm}} = 6$

Fact Families

Write the fact family for the model.

1.

$\underline{7} + \underline{8} = \underline{15}$

$\underline{8} + \underline{7} = \underline{}$

$\underline{15} - \underline{8} = \underline{}$

$\underline{15} - \underline{} = \underline{}$

2.

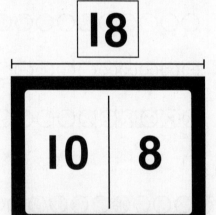

$\underline{} + \underline{} = \underline{}$

$\underline{} + \underline{} = \underline{}$

$\underline{} - \underline{} = \underline{}$

$\underline{} - \underline{} = \underline{}$

Reasoning

Solve the problem.

3. Which related facts
   describe this picture?

Ⓐ $4 + 11 = 15, 15 - 4 = 11$

Ⓑ $11 - 4 = 7, 7 + 4 = 11$

Ⓒ $3 + 7 = 10, 10 - 3 = 7$

Ⓓ $7 - 4 = 3, 7 - 3 = 4$

Using Addition to Subtract

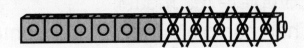

$$6 + 5 = 11 \qquad\qquad 11 - 5 = \underline{6}$$

> You can use an addition fact to help you write a
> subtraction fact with the same numbers.

Add. Then use the addition fact to help you subtract.
Use cubes if you like.

1.

$$4 + 9 = \underline{13}$$

$$13 - 9 = \underline{4}$$

2.

$$8 + 7 = \underline{}$$

$$15 - 7 = \underline{}$$

3.

$$7 + 4 = \underline{}$$

$$11 - 4 = \underline{}$$

4.

$$6 + 7 = \underline{}$$

$$13 - 7 = \underline{}$$

Using Addition to Subtract

Complete the model.
Then complete the number sentences.

1.

$18 - 8 =$ _10_

$8 +$ _____ $= 18$

2.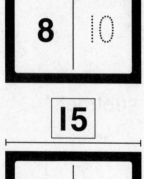

$15 - 6 =$ _____

$6 +$ _____ $= 15$

Algebra

3. Which addition fact will help you solve $14 - 9$?

    Ⓐ $5 + 14 = 19$

    Ⓑ $5 + 9 = 14$

    Ⓒ $4 + 9 = 13$

    Ⓓ $5 + 7 = 12$

Algebra

4. Draw the missing shape. Then explain how you know.

If ◯ + ☐ = △

Then △ − ☐ = ☐

Explain: _____

_____

_____

Subtraction Facts

There are many ways to learn and remember subtraction facts.
One way is think about a related addition fact.

$12 - 8 = ?$

Think: What plus 8 equals 12?
$? + 8 = 12$

Then you can use a number line to help you add.

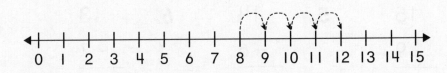

By using the line, I know that $8 + 4 = 12$

Complete the addition fact. Then solve the subtraction fact.
Use the number line to help you.

1.
$$\begin{array}{r} 5 \\ + 6 \\ \hline \end{array} \qquad \begin{array}{r} 11 \\ - 5 \\ \hline \end{array}$$

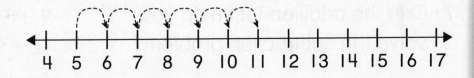

2.
$$\begin{array}{r} 9 \\ + \boxed{} \\ \hline 16 \end{array} \qquad \begin{array}{r} 16 \\ - 9 \\ \hline \end{array}$$

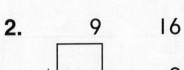

Subtraction Facts

Complete the addition fact.
Then solve the subtraction fact.

1. $16 - 7 = \boxed{}$

$7 + \boxed{} = 16$

2. $14 - 6 = \boxed{}$

$6 + \boxed{} = 14$

Subtract.

3.
$$\begin{array}{r} 17 \\ -\ 8 \\ \hline \boxed{} \end{array}$$

4.
$$\begin{array}{r} 15 \\ -\ 9 \\ \hline \boxed{} \end{array}$$

5.
$$\begin{array}{r} 14 \\ -\ 6 \\ \hline \boxed{} \end{array}$$

6.
$$\begin{array}{r} 13 \\ -\ 7 \\ \hline \boxed{} \end{array}$$

Reasonableness

7. Can the addition fact help you
solve the subtraction problem?

$9 + 9 = 18$

$18 - 9 = ?$

Circle **yes** or **no.**

yes   **no**

Journal

8. Solve $15 - 9$.

Use words, pictures, or numbers
to show how you solved it.

Problem Solving: Draw a Picture and Write a Number Sentence

You can write a number sentence to solve problems.

Avi played 2 games of basketball.
He scored 8 points in the first game.
He scored 6 points in the second game.
How many points did Avi score in all?

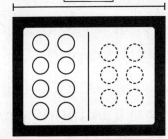

You can draw a picture to help you solve the problem.
Then you can write a number sentence.

$$\underline{8} + \underline{6} = \underline{14}$$

Complete the model.
Then write a number sentence.

1. Gina has 9 books.
   She buys 4 more books.
   How many books
   does Gina have now?

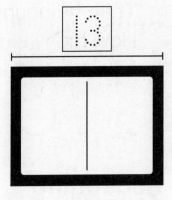

2. Metta sees 15 frogs.
   7 frogs hop away.
   How many frogs
   are left?

Problem Solving: Draw a Picture and Write a Number Sentence

Write a number sentence to solve.
Draw a picture to check your answer.

1. Helen made invitations for her party.
She made 7 invitations on Monday.
She made 6 invitations on Tuesday.
How many invitations
did Helen make in all?

_____ ◯ _____ = _____ invitations

2. Joe started at the bottom
of the stairs.
He hopped up 9 stairs.
Then he hopped down 3 stairs.
How many stairs is Joe
from the bottom?

_____ ◯ _____ = _____ stairs

Reasoning

3. Which number sentence
tells how many apples in all?

Ⓐ   8 − 7 = 1
Ⓑ   8 − 1 = 7
Ⓒ   7 + 1 = 8
Ⓓ   7 + 8 = 15

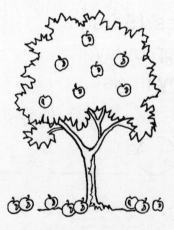

Using Data from Real Graphs

You can use real objects
to make a graph by arranging
the objects in rows and columns.

This is a real-object
graph because the
counters are real
objects.

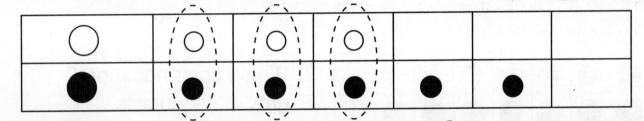

Circle each pair of counters in the graph.

Is there the same number of colors?   Yes   (No)

Which color has more?   (Black)   White

How many counters do not have a partner? 2

I. Circle the correct answers. Write the number.

Is there the same number of colors?   Yes   No

Which color has more?   Black   White

How many counters do not have a partner? _____

Using Data from Real Graphs

Look at the graph. Circle the correct answers.
Write the number.

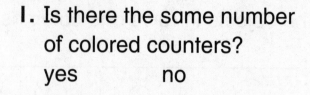

1. Is there the same number
of colored counters?

yes   no

2. Which color has more?

gray   black

3. How many counters do
not have a partner?

_____

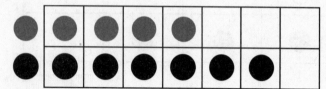

4. Is there the same number of
colored counters?

yes   no

5. Which color has more?

gray   black

6. How many counters do
not have a partner? _____

Journal

7. Draw black counters
on the graph
so I black counter
does not have a partner.

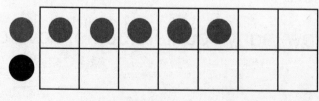

Using Data from Picture Graphs

You can use information in picture graphs to answer questions.

Each party hat stands for 1 vote.

10 children voted.

Favorite Party Hat						
🎉 Stripes	🎉	🎉	🎉	🎉		
🎉 Polka Dots	🎉	🎉	🎉	🎉	🎉	🎉

How many children voted for the hat with stripes? __4__

How many children voted for the hat with polka dots? __6__

Which hat got the most votes?   Stripes   Polka Dots

Favorite Club						
🔍 Science	🔍	🔍	🔍	🔍	🔍	🔍
🖌 Art	🖌	🖌	🖌	🖌	🖌	

1. How many children in all voted for a favorite club? __11__

2. How many children voted for Science Club? _____

3. How many children voted for Art Club? _____

4. Which club got more votes?   Science   Art

Using Data from Picture Graphs

Use the graph to answer the questions.

Favorite Seasons						
☀ Summer	☀	☀	☀	☀	☀	☀
🍁 Fall	🍁	🍁	🍁	🍁		
❄ Winter	❄	❄	❄			
🌷 Spring	🌷	🌷	🌷	🌷	🌷	

I. How many children chose winter? _____

2. Which season is the favorite? _____

3. Which season did 4 children choose? _____

Number Sense

4. How many more children chose summer than spring?

Ⓐ 11

Ⓑ 6

Ⓒ 5

Ⓓ 1

Reasoning

5. What is the graph about?

Ⓐ Favorite Subjects

Ⓑ Summer

Ⓒ Favorite Seasons

Ⓓ Fall

Using Data from Bar Graphs

You can use information in bar graphs to answer questions.

Each shaded square stands for 1 vote. The shaded squares in a row form a bar.

The least favorite shape has the shortest bar.

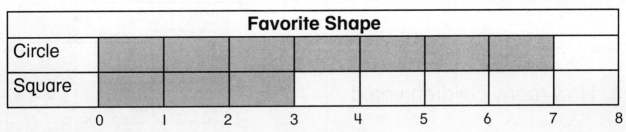

Favorite Shape

How many votes did each shape get?

Circle __7__ Square __3__

Which shape is the favorite? Circle Square

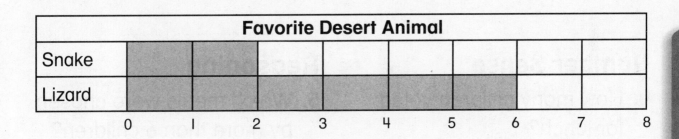

Favorite Desert Animal

1. How many votes did each animal get?

Snake _____ Lizard_____

2. Which animal is the favorite? Snake Lizard

Name_____

Using Data from Bar Graphs

Use the graph to answer the questions.

1. Mrs. Dunne's class made a graph of their favorite meals. Which meal is the least favorite?

_____

2. How many children voted

for breakfast? _____

3. How many more children voted for

dinner than for lunch? _____

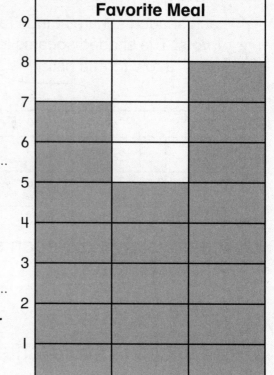

Favorite Meal

Breakfast Lunch Dinner

Number Sense

4. How many children voted for lunch?

(A) 5

(B) 7

(C) 8

(D) 9

Reasoning

5. Which meals were chosen by more than 6 children?

(A) breakfast and lunch

(B) breakfast and dinner

(C) breakfast, lunch, and dinner

(D) lunch and dinner

Location on a Grid

This is a map of Felipe's town.
You want to go from the school to Felipe's house.

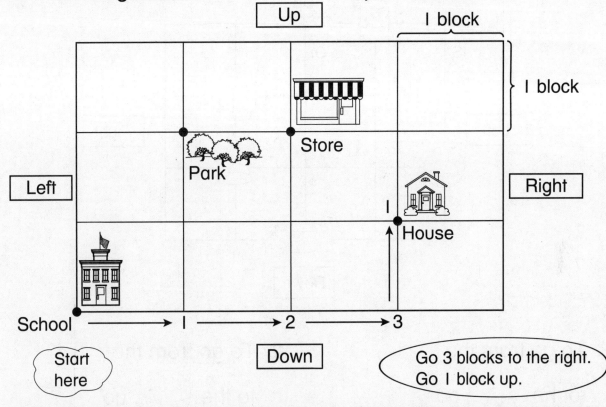

Read the map. Then complete each sentence.

1. To go from the 🏫 to the 🌳🌳🌳 ,

go __1__ block right and __2__ blocks up.

---

2. To go from the 🏠 to the 🏪 ,

go _____ block left and _____ block up.

---

3. To go from the 🏠 to the 🌳🌳🌳 ,

go _____ blocks left and _____ block up.

Name_____

Location on a Grid

Use the grid.

Then complete each sentence.

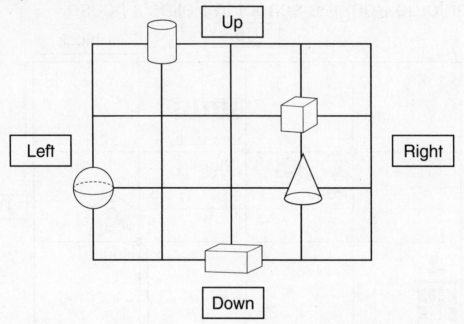

1. To go from the to the , go

_____ spaces right

and _____ spaces down.

2. To go from the to the , go

_____ spaces left

and _____ space up.

Spatial Thinking

3. Which shape is 1 space down
and 3 spaces left from the ?

Ⓐ

Ⓑ

Ⓒ

Ⓓ

Collecting Data
Using Tally Marks

The children made tally marks to show the ways
children get to school.

| equals 1   ⑷⑷ equals 5

count 5 6 7

		Total
Walk	ⅢⅢ ‖	7
School bus	ⅢⅢ ⅢⅢ	10

count 5   10

1. Color some balloons red. Color the rest blue.
   Use tally marks to show how many balloons
   there are in each color. Write the totals.

		Total
Red		
Blue		

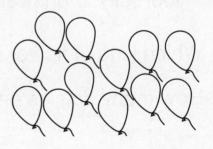

Use the tally chart to answer the questions.

2. Of which color are there the most? _____

3. Of which color are there the fewest? _____

4. How many balloons are there altogether? _____

Collecting Data
Using Tally Marks

Make tally marks to show how many flowers
of each kind there are. Then write each total.

Total

1.

Rose		
Tulip		
Daisy		

Use your tally to answer the questions.

2. Which kind of flower is there the most of? _____

3. How many daisies and roses are there in all? _____

Algebra

4. How many more daises
than tulips are there?

(A) 2
(B) 3
(C) 5
(D) 7

Reasoning

5. How many roses and
tulips are there in all?

(A) 15
(B) 13
(C) 12
(D) 3

Making Real Graphs

You can use a tally chart
to make a real graph.

The chart shows Kim has 5 gray cubes
and 3 white cubes.

Kim's Cubes — Tally Chart		
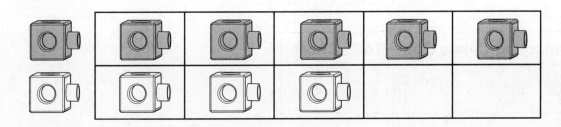	ⷜⷜⷜⷜⷜ	5
					3

How many 🔲 will you put in graph? _5_

How many 🔲 will you put in the graph? _3_

I. Use the tally chart to make
a graph with cubes.

Reba's Cubes — Tally Chart		
🔲	||||	4
🔲	ⷜⷜⷜ		6

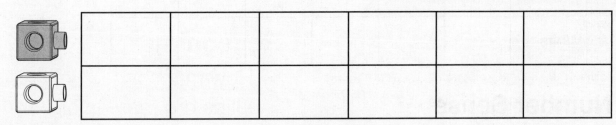

2. If you add I gray cube to the graph,
how many gray cubes will there be? _____ gray cubes

Making Real Graphs

Sarina used cubes to make a
picture of a cow.
She used a tally chart to show how
many cubes of each color she used
in her picture.

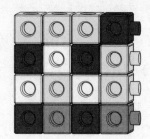

1. Use the tally chart to make a graph.

Connecting Cubes Cow—Tally Chart

⬛	Black	卌	5
🟩	Green	‖	2
🟦	Blue	卌 |	6
⬜	White	‖|	3

Connecting Cubes Cow—Real Graph

Black					
Green					
Blue					
White					

Number Sense

2. Sarina adds 4 more green cubes to her picture.
How many green cubes are there now?

10	9	7	6
Ⓐ	Ⓑ	Ⓒ	Ⓓ

Making Picture Graphs

You can use a tally chart
to make a picture graph.

Draw a flower for each tally mark.

Favorite Flower	
🌼	‖‖‖
🌷	‖‖

Favorite Flower					
🌼 Daisy	🌼	🌼	🌼	🌼	🌼
🌷 Tulip	🌷	🌷	🌷		

In how many boxes did you draw a daisy? __5__

In how many boxes did you draw a tulip? __3__

Which flower is the favorite? __daisy__

I. Ask your friends to vote for
apple juice or milk as their
favorite drink.
Make a tally chart and
a picture graph.

Favorite Drink	
🧃	
🥛	

🧃 Apple Juice					
🥛 Milk					

2. How many of your friends voted for apple juice? _____

3. Which drink is the favorite? _____

Making Picture Graphs

Favorite Items to Collect	Tally Marks	Totals
Shells	|||	3
Stamps	|||||		6
Coins	||||	4

I. Use the information in the tally chart.
Draw pictures to make a picture graph.

Favorite Items to Collect						
Shells						
Stamps						
Coins						

2. Which item is the least favorite to collect? _____

3. Write the items in order from most favored to least favored.

_____   _____   _____

most favored   least favored

Number Sense

4. How many more people chose
stamps than coins?

10   6   4   2
Ⓐ   Ⓑ   Ⓒ   Ⓓ

Problem Solving: Make a Graph

Each square that is colored gray equals 1 child's selection.

Name of Fairy-Tail Characters

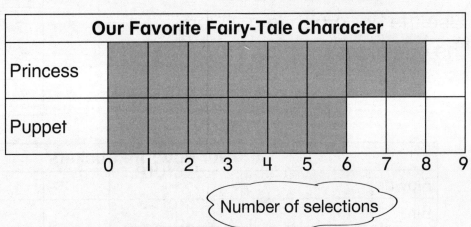

Our Favorite Fairy-Tale Character

Princess

Puppet

0 1 2 3 4 5 6 7 8 9

Number of selections

Look at the number of squares colored for the princess.

How many squares are colored? __8__

Look at the number of squares colored for the puppet.

How many squares are colored? __6__

Circle the favorite fairy-tale character of the children.

Princess   Puppet

1. Ask your classmates to select their favorite snack.
   Color to make a bar graph. Then answer the questions.

Yogurt									
Fruit									

0 1 2 3 4 5 6 7 8 9

2. Which snack is the favorite? _____

3. How many children selected fruit? _____

Problem Solving:
Make a Graph

The chart shows what kinds of
stickers the children like.
Use the bar graph to answer
the questions.

Favorite Stickers		
	Flower	2
	Bird	4
	Boat	7
	Dog	3

Our Favorite Stickers

Flower								
Bird								
Boat								
Dog								

0   1   2   3   4   5   6   7   8

1. Which sticker do children like the most? _____

2. Which sticker do children like the least? _____

3. Number Sense

Which of the following shows the stickers in order from
most favorite to least favorite?

Ⓐ   dog, boat, bird, flower

Ⓑ   flower, dog, bird, boat

Ⓒ   flower, bird, boat, dog

Ⓓ   boat, bird, dog, flower

Certain or Impossible

 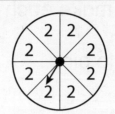

This spinner has only 3s on it.

This spinner has no 3s on it.

I am certain
to land on a 3.

It is impossible
for me to land on 3.

Are you certain to land on 4 or is it impossible?

1.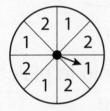

certain

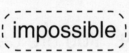 impossible

2.

certain

impossible

Are you certain to land on black or is it impossible?

3.

certain

impossible

4.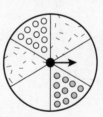

certain

impossible

Color the cubes so that the sentence is true.

5. It is impossible to
pick a red cube.

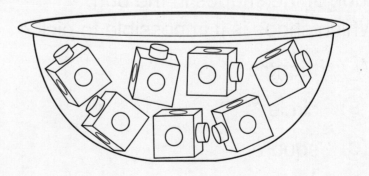

Name_____

Certain or Impossible

Color the cubes to make each sentence true.

1. You are certain to pick a green cube.

2. It is impossible to pick a red cube.

3. It is impossible to pick a blue cube.

4. You are certain to pick a yellow cube.

Spatial Reasoning

5. Look at the shapes in the bag. Which shape is it impossible to pick?

Ⓐ triangle

Ⓑ circle

Ⓒ square

Ⓓ hexagon

Likely or Unlikely

There are more gray cubes in the bag than there are white cubes.

Pick a cube.
Make a tally mark.
Put the cube back
in the bag. Pick
another cube.
Make a tally mark.
Put the cube back
in the bag.

Color	Tally
Gray	||
White	

Since there are more gray cubes in the bag, it is more likely you will pick gray.

Fill a bag with 10 blue and 3 red cubes.
Pick a cube. Mark a tally for your pick.
Put the cube back. Do this 10 times.
Mark a tally for each pick.

I.

Color	Tally
Blue	
Red	

2. Predict: Which color cube is it more likely you will pick next?

_____

Likely or Unlikely

Look at the tally chart and spinner.
Answer the questions.

1.

Likely and Unlikely Colors	
Color	Tally
Gray	||||
White	|||| |||

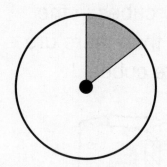

Which color is the spinner
likely to land on? _____

2.

Likely and Unlikely Colors	
Color	Tally
Gray	|||| |
White	|||| |||| ||

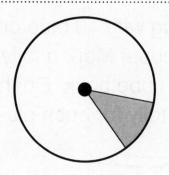

Which color is the spinner
unlikely to land on? _____

Algebra

3. Tess spins this spinner 10 times.
It lands on gray 4 times.
How many times does it land on white?

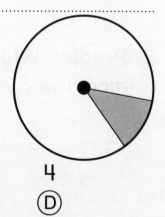

14
Ⓐ

10
Ⓑ

6
Ⓒ

4
Ⓓ

Making Equal Parts

This apple pie is divided into equal parts.

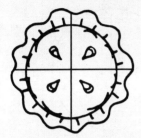

Each part is the same size.

There are ___4___ equal parts.

This apple pie is **not** divided into equal parts.

Each part is **not** the same size.

There are ___0___ equal parts.

Write the number of equal parts on each shape.

1.

There are ___3___ equal parts.

2.

There are _____ equal parts.

3.

There are _____ equal parts.

4.

There are _____ equal parts.

5.

There are _____ equal parts.

6.

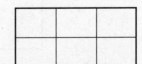

There are _____ equal parts.

Name_____

Making Equal Parts

Write how many equal parts the shape has.
If the parts are not equal, write 0.

1.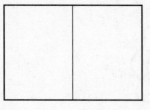

_____ equal parts

2.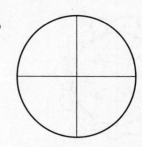

_____ equal parts

3.

_____ equal parts

4.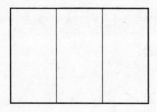

_____ equal parts

5.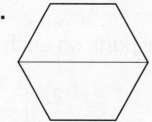

_____ equal parts

6.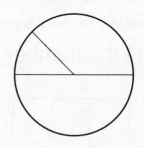

_____ equal parts

Journal

7. Draw straight lines to divide these
shapes into the equal parts listed.

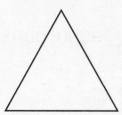

2 equal parts

4 equal parts

2 equal parts

Describing Equal Parts
of Whole Objects

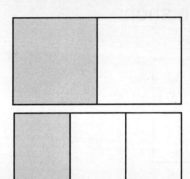 This rectangle has 2 equal parts.
I out of 2 equal parts is shaded.

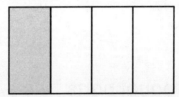

I out of 3 equal parts is shaded.   I out of 4 equal parts is shaded.

I. Circle the shape that shows I out of 3 equal parts shaded.

---

2. Circle the shape that shows I out of 4 equal parts shaded.

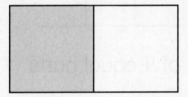   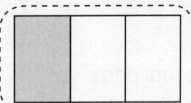

---

3. Circle the shape that shows 3 out of 4 equal parts shaded.

Describing Equal Parts of Whole Objects

Color the given number of equal parts in each shape.

1.

I out of 3 equal parts

2.

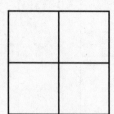

3 out of 4 equal parts

3.

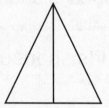

I out of 2 equal parts

4.

2 out of 4 equal parts

Spatial Thinking

5. Which picture shows 2 out of 3 equal parts shaded?

Ⓐ

Ⓑ

Ⓒ

Ⓓ

Number Sense

6. How many fourths equal one whole?

Ⓐ 4

Ⓑ 3

Ⓒ 2

Ⓓ I

Making Parts of a Set

| There are 2 balls in all.

I out of 2 balls is gray.

 | There are 3 balls in all.

I out of 3 balls is gray.

 | There are 4 balls in all.

I out of 4 balls is gray.

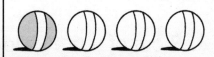 |

Tell how many are gray. Tell how many in all.

1.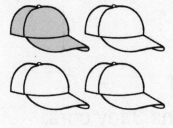

_____ cap is gray.

There are __4__ caps in all.

__1__ out of __4__ is gray.

2.

_____ doll is gray.

There are _____ dolls in all.

_____ out of _____ is gray.

3.

_____ yo-yo is gray.

There are _____ yo-yos in all.

_____ out of _____ is gray.

Making Parts of a Set

Color to show the part.

1. 1 out of 4 is shaded.

2. 1 out of 2 is red.

3. 3 out of 4 are yellow.

4. 2 out of 3 are green.

Spatial Thinking

5. Which picture shows 2 out of 4 shaded?

Ⓐ

Ⓑ

Ⓒ

Ⓓ

Algebra

6. June has 3 toy cars. 1 out of her 3 cars is green. Which part of the group is not green?

Ⓐ 1 out of 2 cars

Ⓑ 1 out of 3 cars

Ⓒ 2 out of 3 cars

Ⓓ 2 out of 4 cars

Describing Parts of Sets

You can use numbers to describe parts of a set.
Count the gray socks. Write the number.

_____ socks are gray.

Count how many socks in all.
Write the number.

There are _____ socks in all.

Use your numbers to describe the set.

_____ out of _____ socks are gray.

Circle the sentence that tells what part of the picture is gray.

1. 1 out of 2

(1 out of 3)

2. 1 out of 2

1 out of 4

3. 1 out of 4

3 out of 4

4. 2 out of 3

2 out of 5

5. 1 out of 2

1 out of 4

6. 5 out of 6

4 out of 6

Describing Parts of Sets

Describe each picture.
Write the numbers.

1. _____ out of _____
are small.

2. _____ out of _____
is gray.

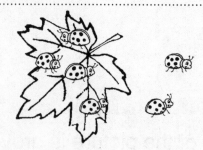

3. _____ out of _____
are on the leaf.

4. _____ out of _____
have nuts.

Reasoning

5. 3 of Joel's 4 pets are lizards. Which picture could show all of his pets?

Ⓐ

Ⓑ

Ⓒ

Ⓓ

Reasonableness

6. Tara has 7 friends. Most of her friends are girls. Which sentence tells about Tara's friends?

Ⓐ 2 out of 7 are girls.

Ⓑ 3 out of 7 are boys.

Ⓒ 4 out of 7 are boys.

Ⓓ 6 out of 7 are girls.

Practice 19-4

Problem Solving:
Draw a Picture

You can draw a picture to solve a problem.

Mario has 3 shirts.
2 of his shirts have stripes.
What part of the group has stripes?

First draw all the shirts Mario has.
Then draw stripes on 2 of his shirts.

___2___ out of ___3___ shirts have stripes.

1. Julia has 4 apples.
   3 apples are red.
   1 apple is green.
   What part of the group is green?
   Draw a picture to show the fruit.

   _____ out of ___4___ apples are green.

2. Jacob picks 5 flowers.
   2 of the flowers are yellow.
   3 of the flowers are red.
   What part of the group is red?
   Draw a picture to show the flowers.

   _____ out of _____ flowers are red.

Problem Solving:
Draw a Picture

Read each story.
Draw a picture. Write the numbers.

1. Fred has 4 toy boats.

3 boats have sails.

What part of the group has sails?

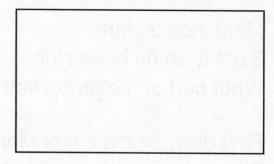

_____ out of _____ have sails.

2. Mr. Novak has 2 shirts.

1 shirt has a pocket.

What part of the group
has pockets?

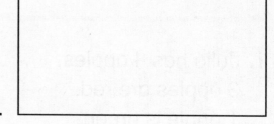

_____ out of _____ has pockets.

Reasoning

3. There are 3 books on the shelf.

Kate reads 2 books.

Which picture shows the part that Kate read?

Ⓐ

Ⓑ

Ⓒ

Ⓓ

Adding Groups of 10

You can use what you know about adding ones
to add groups of ten.

2 ones and 5 ones are 7 ones.   2 tens and 5 tens are 7 tens.

   2   +   5   =   7   20   +   50   =   70

Write each number sentence.

1.

_3_ + _2_ = _5_   _30_ + _20_ = _50_

2.

___ + ___ = _6_   ___ + ___ = _60_

3.

___ + ___ = ___   ___ + ___ = ___

4.

___ + ___ = ___

5.

___ + ___ = ___

Adding Groups of 10

Write numbers to complete each number sentence.

1.

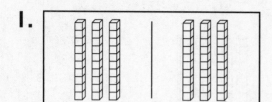

_____ tens + _____ tens = _____ tens

_____ + _____ = _____

Complete each number sentence.

2. 50 + 20 = _____

3. 30 + 40 = _____

4. 20 + 30 = _____

5. 70 + 20 = _____

6. 60 + 30 = _____

7. 10 + 80 = _____

Number Sense

8. David has 2 books of stamps.
The first book has 50 stamps.
The other book has 30 stamps.
How many stamps does David have in all?

Ⓐ 20

Ⓑ 70

Ⓒ 80

Ⓓ 90

Adding Tens on a Hundred Chart

1	2	3	4	5	⑥	7	8	9	10
11	12	13	14	15	16	17	18	19	20
21	22	23	24	25	26	27	28	29	30
31	32	33	34	35	36	37	38	39	40
41	42	43	44	45	46	47	48	49	50
51	52	53	54	55	56	57	58	59	60
61	62	63	64	65	66	67	68	69	70
71	72	73	74	75	76	77	78	79	80
81	82	83	84	85	86	87	88	89	90
91	92	93	94	95	96	97	98	99	100

When you add tens on a hundred chart, you skip count by tens. The ones digit in each number is the same as the ones digit in the number you started from.

The tens digit of each number is one more than the tens digit of the number before it.

Use the hundred chart to add tens to 16.

1. 16
$+ 10$
26

2. 16
$+ 20$

3. 16
$+ 30$

4. 16
$+ 40$

5. What numbers did you skip count on the hundred chart to find the answers? _____

Algebra

6. Fill in the missing digits to complete the pattern.

5____, 62, _____2, _____2

Adding Tens on a Hundred Chart

1	2	3	4	5	6	7	8	9	10
11	12	13	14	15	16	17	18	19	20
21	22	23	24	25	26	27	28	29	30
31	32	33	34	35	36	37	38	39	40
41	42	43	44	45	46	47	48	49	50
51	52	53	54	55	56	57	58	59	60
61	62	63	64	65	66	67	68	69	70
71	72	73	74	75	76	77	78	79	80
81	82	83	84	85	86	87	88	89	90
91	92	93	94	95	96	97	98	99	100

Use the hundred chart to add tens.

1. 24 + 30 = _____   56 + 20 = _____   13 + 70 = _____

2. 11 + 80 = _____   67 + 10 = _____   39 + 40 = _____

Algebra

3. Which number sentence is equal to 24 + 10?

    Ⓐ   14 + 10

    Ⓑ   14 + 20

    Ⓒ   24 + 20

    Ⓓ   34 + 10

Adding Tens to Two-Digit Numbers

You can count on by tens to add.

3 tens

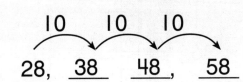

28 + 30   is   28 + 3 tens   28,   _38_   _48_,   _58_

$$28 + 30 = 58$$

Solve each number sentence.

10   10   10   10   10

1.   31, _41_ _51_, _61_, _71_, _81_

31 + 50 is 31 + _5_ tens

$$31 + 50 = \_81\_$$

2.   52, _____ _____

52 + 20 is 52 + _____ tens

$$52 + 20 = \_\_\_$$

3.   33, _____, _____, _____, _____

33 + 40 is 33 + _____ tens

$$33 + 40 = \_\_\_$$

Name_____

20-3

Adding Tens to Two-Digit Numbers

Write each number sentence.

1.

_____ + _____ = _____

2.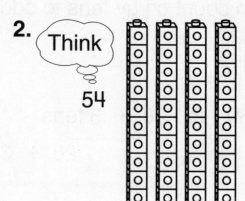

_____ + _____ = _____

3.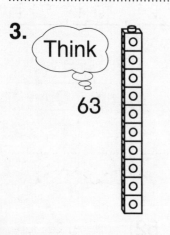

_____ + _____ = _____

4.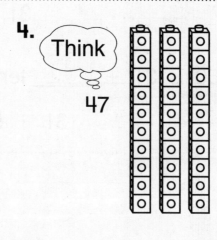

_____ + _____ = _____

Number Sense

5. Will has 24 crayons.
He gets 4 more boxes of crayons.
Each box has 10 crayons.
How many crayons does Will have now?

64
(A)

54
(B)

44
(C)

34
(D)

Practice **20-3**

© Pearson Education, Inc. 1

Adding to a Two-Digit Number

Add 26 and 5.

Show 26.   Add 5.   Regroup 10 ones as 1 ten.

Tens	Ones

Tens	Ones

Tens	Ones

Tens	Ones

$$26 + 5 = \underline{31}$$

Find the sum.

1. Add 16 and 7.

Show 16.   Add 7.   Regroup.   Find the sum.

Tens	Ones

Tens	Ones

Tens	Ones

Tens	Ones

$$16 + 7 = \underline{23}$$

2. Add 28 and 5.

Show 28.   Add 5.   Regroup.   Find the sum.

Tens	Ones

Tens	Ones

Tens	Ones

Tens	Ones

$$28 + 5 = \underline{}$$

Adding to a Two-Digit Number

Write the sum.

Find the sum.	**Do you need to regroup?**

1. 27 + 6 = _33_ (yes)   no

2. 43 + 5 = _____   yes   no

3. 34 + 8 = _____   yes   no

4. 17 + 4 = _____   yes   no

5. 56 + 3 = _____   yes   no

6. 93 + 2 = _____   yes   no

7. 87 + 7 = _____   yes   no

8. 68 + 5 = _____   yes   no

9. 36 + 3 = _____   yes   no

10. Journal There are 24 counters.
How many counters could you add
without having to regroup? Why?

_____

_____

Subtracting Tens on a Hundred Chart

1	2	3	4	5	6	7	8	9	10
11	12	13	14	15	16	17	18	19	20
21	22	23	24	25	26	27	28	29	30
31	32	33	34	35	36	37	38	39	40
41	42	43	44	45	46	47	48	49	50
51	52	53	54	55	56	57	58	59	60
61	62	63	64	65	66	67	68	69	70
71	72	73	74	75	76	77	78	79	80
81	82	83	84	85	86	87	88	89	90
91	92	93	94	95	96	97	98	99	100

To subtract by tens, you can count back by tens on a hundred chart. Move up a row for each ten you subtract. All of the numbers will end in the same number.

$41 - 30 =$ _____

Count back by tens on the hundred chart to subtract.

1. 84
  $- 60$
  $\boxed{24}$

2. 59
  $- 10$
  $\boxed{}$

3. 45
  $- 30$
  $\boxed{}$

4. 78
  $- 40$
  $\boxed{}$

5. What numbers did you skip count on
the hundred chart to find the answers? _____

Algebra

6. Fill in the missing digits to complete the pattern.

8_____, 72, _____2, _____2

Reteaching 20-5

Subtracting Tens on a Hundred Chart

1	2	3	4	5	6	7	8	9	10
11	12	13	14	15	16	17	18	19	20
21	22	23	24	25	26	27	28	29	30
31	32	33	34	35	36	37	38	39	40
41	42	43	44	45	46	47	48	49	50
51	52	53	54	55	56	57	58	59	60
61	62	63	64	65	66	67	68	69	70
71	72	73	74	75	76	77	78	79	80
81	82	83	84	85	86	87	88	89	90
91	92	93	94	95	96	97	98	99	100

Use the hundred chart to subtract tens.

1. $87 - 40 =$ _____ $53 - 30 =$ _____ $71 - 60 =$ _____

2. $98 - 10 =$ _____ $32 - 20 =$ _____ $83 - 50 =$ _____

3. $43 - 20 =$ _____ $71 - 50 =$ _____ $66 - 40 =$ _____

Algebra

4. Which number completes the subtraction sentence?

$75 -$ _____ $= 35$

- (A) 20
- (B) 30
- (C) 40
- (D) 50

Subtracting Tens from Two-Digit Numbers

You can count back by tens to subtract.

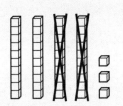

2 tens
10   10

43, __33__, __23__

43 − 20   is   43 − 2 tens

43 − 20 = __23__

Solve each number sentence.

1.

10

34, __24__

34 − 10   is   34 − __1__ ten

34 − 10 = __24__

2.

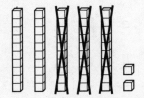

10

52, _____, _____, _____

52 − 30   is   52 − _____ tens

52 − 30 = _____

3.

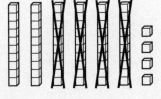

64, _____, _____, _____, _____

64 − 40   is   64 − _____ tens

64 − 40 = _____

Subtracting Tens from Two-Digit Numbers

Cross out the tens. Write the difference.

1.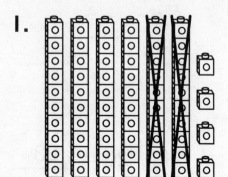

$$64 - 20 = \underline{\hspace{2cm}}$$

2.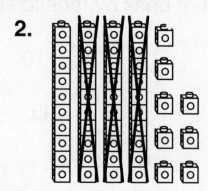

$$47 - 30 = \underline{\hspace{2cm}}$$

3.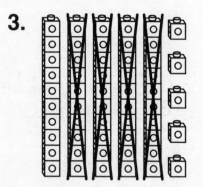

$$55 - 40 = \underline{\hspace{2cm}}$$

4.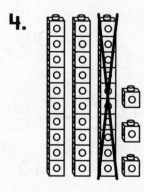

$$33 - 10 = \underline{\hspace{2cm}}$$

Journal

5. Roberto says that $75 - 30 = 35$.
Is Roberto correct?
Explain.

_____

_____

Subracting from a Two-Digit Number

Find the difference for the problem 32 − 6.

Show 32.

Tens	Ones

Subtract 6.

Regroup 1 ten as 10 ones.

Tens	Ones

Subtract.

Tens	Ones

32 − 6 = 26

---

1. Find the difference for the problem 46 − 8.

Show 46.

Tens	Ones

Subtract 8.

Regroup.

Tens	Ones

Subtract.

Tens	Ones

46 − 8 = 38

---

2. Find the difference for the problem 23 − 7.

Show 23.

Tens	Ones

Subtract 7.

Regroup.

Tens	Ones

Subtract.

Tens	Ones

23 − 7 =

Subtracting from a Two-Digit Number

Write the difference.

Find the difference.	**Do you need to regroup?**
1. 42 − 6 = _36_	⟨yes⟩ no
2. 37 − 5 = _____	yes no
3. 62 − 4 = _____	yes no
4. 58 − 9 = _____	yes no
5. 24 − 7 = _____	yes no
6. 77 − 6 = _____	yes no
7. 85 − 8 = _____	yes no
8. 93 − 3 = _____	yes no

Spatial Thinking

9. Draw cubes to show the same number in both place value mats.

Tens	Ones		Tens	Ones

Problem Solving:
Extra Information

Sometimes a problem has information you do not need.
When you solve a problem, you need to find what information
you do and do not need.

Karl has 52 baseball cards.
~~He has 37 baseball stickers.~~
His mom gives him 26 more cards.
How many cards does he have in all?

Underline the information you need.
Cross out the information you do not need.
Then write a number sentence to solve.

$\underline{52} + \underline{26} = \underline{78}$ baseball cards

Read the problem.
Cross out the information you do not need.
Then write a number sentence to solve.

1. ~~David helped his dad sort DVDs and CDs.~~
   There were 38 new DVDs.
   There were 21 used DVDs.
   How many DVDs in all?

   _____ + _____ = _____ DVDs

2. There are 42 pink roses
   in the garden.
   There are 18 yellow daisies.
   There are 47 red roses.
   How many roses are there?

   _____ + _____ = _____ roses

Problem Solving:
Extra Information

Cross out the extra information.
Write a number sentence to solve the problem.
You can use cubes or a hundred chart to help.

1. There are 16 boys on Milo's flag
football team.
In their first game, they scored 14 points.
In their second game, they scored 28 points. +
How many points did the team score in all?

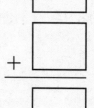

points

2. Ms. Patel teaches tap dance and ballet.
There are 9 girls in her tap class.
All the girls are 6 years old.
There are 7 girls in her ballet class. +
How many girls are there in all?

girls

Reasoning

3. One tank of goldfish has 35 fish.
The other tank of goldfish has 42 fish.
A goldfish that is cared for can live
15 years or more.
How many fish are in both tanks?
Which sentence is extra information?

   Ⓐ   One tank of goldfish has 35 fish.

   Ⓑ   The other tank of goldfish has 42 fish.

   Ⓒ   A goldfish that is cared for can live 15 years or more.

   Ⓓ   How many fish are in both tanks?